Tales from the Jesse Tree

Tales from the Jesse Tree

25 Bible stories to watch, tell and explore

Amy Robinson

Foreword by Bob Hartman

www.kevinmayhew.com

First published in Great Britain in 2014 by Kevin Mayhew Ltd
Buxhall, Stowmarket, Suffolk IP14 3BW
Tel: +44 (0) 1449 737978 Fax: +44 (0) 1449 737834
E-mail: info@kevinmayhew.com

www.kevinmayhew.com

9 8 7 6 5 4 3 2 1 0

ISBN 978 1 84867 717 3
Catalogue No. 1501441

Cover design by Rob Mortonson
© Images used under licence from Shutterstock Inc.
Edited by Nicki Copeland
Typeset by Richard Weaver

Printed and bound in Great Britain

For Abigail and Jeremy

Tales
from the
Jesse
Tree

Contents

About the author   9

Foreword by Bob Hartman   10

Introduction   12

How to use this book   14

Advent timetables   16

Story 1   Creation   17

Story 2   Adam and Eve   20

Story 3   Noah   24

Story 4   Abraham   28

Story 5   Rebekah   34

Story 6   Jacob   38

Story 7   Joseph   43

Story 8   Miriam and Moses   48

Story 9   Moses and the burning bush   53

Story 10   The journey   58

Story 11   The ten commandments   62

Story 12   Rahab   65

Story 13   Joshua   70

Story 14   Ruth   74

Story 15   Samuel   79

Story 16   Jesse's sons   84

Story 17   David and Goliath   88

Story 18   David writes a song   92

Story 19   Elijah   96

Story 20   Jonah   100

Story 21   Isaiah   107

Story 22   Jeremiah   111

Story 23   John the Baptist   114

Story 24   Mary   117

Bonus Story

Story 25   Christmas Day   124

Acknowledgements   127

About the author

Amy Robinson is a writer, performance storyteller and ventriloquist. As co-founder of *Snail Tales* she has been telling all sorts of stories in all sorts of places for six years, and is the benefice children's worker at her own church. She lives in a rectory in Suffolk with the rector, two children and several puppets.

Foreword

by Bob Hartman

I was leading a workshop recently, and I asked the participants to tell me what they were looking for in Bible-based books for children. One woman said that her child had received several children's Bibles for her confirmation. They were beautiful, the woman explained, but they never came down from the shelf because the child didn't find them particularly interesting to read.

Sad, I know. And unfortunately that is too often the case – where the emphasis is on a traditional 'look' and 'feel' and not on a retelling that is child friendly and compelling.

But here's the good news (in every sense!). There's a bit of a 'Retelling Revolution' going on at the moment. And the book you have in your hands will most definitely come down from the shelf, because here Amy retells a collection of Bible stories that children will enjoy hearing and that adults will love to tell.

I say 'hearing'. Bad word. Amy is a storyteller, and she knows that 'hearing' is just a part of what happens when a story is told. Ideally, the eyes and the body (and every other sense, if possible) are engaged as well, so that the story sinks down deep into the child. Amy's storytelling experience shines through these tales. She uses every tool in the storyteller's toolbox to bring these stories to life. And her easy-to-follow instructions will help you to use them too – whether you have years of experience as a storyteller or are just getting started. What's more, the book offers a link to a series of videos, so you can see Amy in action and learn, first-hand, what effective storytelling looks like.

None of those techniques would make much difference, though, if these stories were boring, uninteresting and smelling of 'been-there-done-that'. Fortunately, these stories have been written by someone who loves the written word and who loves the word of God (again, in every sense!). And that means that there is a joy in these retellings that both respects the text and delights in bringing it to life. That's not a contradiction (as some suppose). In fact, respect for the text demands the kind of creativity, wit and playfulness that you will find here.

And what better place to find it than in the Jesse Tree – an age-old tradition that has been used for centuries to trace God's salvation story? It's a storytelling device all of its own, designed for a pre-literate culture, to appeal to eye and ear and touch. And it finds a new life for a different time in Amy's book.

So, enjoy! That's my advice to you. Enjoy reading these stories and sharing these stories with others and seeing what happens when God's story gets told, and told well.

And as for the shelf? No worries. This book is so useful, I suspect it won't find its way there in the first place!

Bob Hartman

Introduction

What is a Jesse Tree?

The term 'Jesse Tree' comes from the eleventh chapter of the book of Isaiah, in which the prophet compares the royal line of King David (son of Jesse) to a fallen tree, but predicts that a new branch will eventually grow from the same family and introduce a reign of peace. Christians believe that Isaiah was looking forward to the birth of Jesus, a descendant of King David. Images of the Jesse Tree can be found in medieval art, in illuminated manuscripts, carvings and stained glass windows. It became a way to depict the genealogy of Jesus and the history of God's interaction with his people leading up to the birth of Christ. The most elaborate versions were a visual treasury of essential Old Testament stories, designed not only as decoration but as an aid to worship and teaching for a mostly illiterate population.

Today, the Jesse Tree has found a new lease of life as a fresh take on the Advent calendar. Every day in Advent, families hang a new symbol on a tree in their homes, until the fully decorated tree adds to the Christmas celebrations. Often, each symbol is accompanied by a Bible verse, telling the story of the events leading from Creation up to the first Christmas.

What is storytelling?

Storytelling is probably the oldest art form in existence. A performance art in its own right, it has seen something of a return to popularity in recent years, especially as workers in education have discovered its value in building literacy skills. Performance storytelling is all about encouraging and nurturing the imagination: the act of creation becomes a shared experience between the performer and the audience. Stories appear without book or script and are performed with simple, plain, multifunctional props or none at all in a return to the open-ended imaginative play that is rapidly becoming lost to screens and prescriptive plastic playsets.

Storytelling is completely accessible. No parent needs special training to tell a bedtime tale from memory. Hopefully the tips and examples given in this book will inspire you to rediscover a skill that is already at your fingertips.

What is this book for?

Tales from the Jesse Tree contains 25 Bible stories, one for each day of the Advent Jesse Tree if that is the way you choose to use them. Each story is accompanied by notes on its place in the biblical narrative, as well as notes on various storytelling techniques that could be used to perform it. There are example videos of each story being told, which could be watched by a family or in a classroom, school assembly or church. These can be found at www.kevinmayhew.com/jesse-videos, using the password 1501441 and are also available on DVD from Kevin Mayhew.[1]

Some of the stories are told through the medium of song. Backing tracks for these are available via the website. Individual links to each song will be provided with each story.

Whether you work through the stories in order or dip in every now and then, I hope you and your children enjoy discovering both the art of storytelling and the wonder of the Jesse Tree story together.

---

1. www.kevinmayhew.com

How to use this book

This book and its accompanying story videos will take you through 25 stories, one for each day of the Advent Jesse Tree, but that doesn't mean you have to watch them all or use them in order! The stories have been carefully chosen so that they can be used all year round, in families, classrooms, Sundays schools, all-age services and anywhere else you can think of.

In each chapter, you will find the following sections:

Introduction

Introduces the story with a brief overview and places it within the biblical narrative.

Story

The script for the story is provided so that it can be read aloud or adapted for your own telling. Due to the improvisational nature of storytelling, the script may not follow the video word for word and is bound to change a little according to you and your audience, which is what storytelling is all about. Don't be afraid to adapt, or to use the techniques and ideas behind one story to tell a completely different one.

Notes for storytellers

In this section, notes are given on the particular methods used in the telling of the story.

From screen to stage

Storytelling is an interactive experience which does not always translate perfectly to video. This section contains suggestions of ways to expand the video performances for the enjoyment of a live audience.

Bible references

This section will help you to find the story, as well as any linked passages, in the Bible.

Decoration

If you are using this book to create your own Advent Jesse Tree, this section will give some suggestions for symbols to represent this story on a decoration for the tree.

What next?

Whether you are using this book in school or at home, this section may offer further learning ideas, craft ideas, music suggestions or links to develop the themes in relation to other parts of the curriculum.

* * *

These sections are to help you use this resource as it suits you best, whether you want to learn techniques for telling the stories yourself, watch the videos as an Advent calendar or use the readings as a springboard to a related topic in the classroom.

Finally, it should be noted that, for convenience, the term 'children' is sometimes used when referring to those listening to the story. That should by no means imply that these stories are meant only for children. The various styles of the tales lend themselves to different age groups, but they are all open to adaptation, and in my experience it is surprising how willingly adults participate in the 'children's' part of an all-age service! The words 'audience' and 'congregation' are also used interchangeably, in recognition of the many different contexts in which these stories can be told. Storytelling is for everybody.

Advent timetables

In a church or a school setting, you may only be able to use this resource once a week. In this case, one way to make the best of the stories might be to match them to the themes of the Advent wreath tradition on the four Sundays of Advent: the first candle to be lit is for God's people or the patriarchs, the second for the prophets, the third is for John the Baptist and the fourth is for Mary. There are several choices of stories that would match this pattern and still retain a strong thematic link between them. For example:

Week One: Abraham (Story 4)
Week Two: Elijah (Story 19)
Week Three: John the Baptist (Story 23)
Week Four: Mary (Story 24)

In this example, there are strong links to be explored involving God's promises, sacrifice and stories of special births: all good Advent themes to lead up to the Nativity.

To create a similar timetable, you might find the following groupings useful:

- Stories 3–7 are about the patriarchs. (For the theme of God's people, stories 1–13 could be used.)
- Stories 19–22 are about prophets.
- Story 23 is about John the Baptist, and Story 24 is about Mary.
- Stories 14–18, including Ruth and David, explore the royal genealogy of Jesus and could be combined with story 21, Isaiah's mention of the Jesse Tree, to make a single set.

The resource also includes two sets of stories, so you could spend four weeks looking at the life of Moses (Stories 8–11). Where the final week of Advent is part of the school holiday, you could opt to spend three weeks focusing on the childhood of King David (Stories 16–18).

Creation

Introduction

The creation story is the essential first tale for an understanding of God's relationship with the world he made and with his people. So much more than an account of how the Earth came into being, the story teaches us about the character of God as creative, powerful and generous, yet caring about details and the lives of people.

Story

You will need: a laundry basket, three blue sheets or towels, a green blanket or towel, a piece of fabric that looks like the night sky and any clothes or bits of fabric you can find to represent plants and animals. Lastly, two little figures to be Adam and Eve.

In the beginning, there was nothing but chaos! *(Dump out the laundry basket.)* Everything was watery and dark. Then God said, 'Let there be light!' *(Lift the basket off the top of the pile of laundry.)* And there was. God said that it was good. And that was the first ever day.

On the second ever day, God picked up some of the water and put it up in the air. *(Pick off the first blue sheet and hang it up somewhere.)* He called that water 'sky' and the water below 'sea'. And he said that it was good.

On the third ever day, God pulled the land up out of the water and made mountains and continents. *(Pull the green fabric up from between the two pieces of blue fabric.)* He also made the land start to grow plants, like trees and bushes and flowers. *(Arrange some clothes as plants or trees.)* And God said that it was good.

On the fourth ever day, God put stars and planets into the sky, and he arranged the sun and the moon. *(Add the starry fabric to the sky.)* And he said that it was good.

On the fifth ever day, God put fish and swimmy things into the sea *(add socks or mittens for fish)* and feathery birds and flappy things into the sky *(how about a feather boa?)*, and he said that it was good.

On the sixth ever day, God invented animals! He made scales and stripes, spots and fur and wool *(add some different textures, colours and animal prints, or soft toys)*, and he said that it was good. Then he made people – a man and a woman called Adam and Eve, to look after it all. *(Place the two figures.)* And God said that it was all very good.

On the seventh ever day, God rested and enjoyed the world he had made. It was the end of the very first week. And it was good.

Notes for storytellers

The only preparation needed to tell this story is to wander around the house with a laundry basket and find appropriate bits of clothing, scarves, blankets and soft toys. As creator both of the story and the laundry picture, you are taking on the voice of God in the story, but don't try to personify him too much, or you'll end up with too human an image. The audience's attention should be fixed on the growing picture.

From screen to stage

Because everything is laid out on the floor, this story is best told to a fairly small group so they can all gather around the area where the picture is being built. With a live audience you can really take your time: why not see if the children can guess what each item might become, or invite them to arrange it themselves in the picture? You can also make it into a sensory tale, passing around the different textures to be explored.

Bible references

This is the creation story taken from Genesis 1–2:3. You may also like to read a more detailed account of the creation of Adam and Eve in Genesis 2:7-25.

Decoration

A globe; a picture of the finished garden of Eden; Adam and Eve.

What next?

The story of creation is an ideal fit with the SEAL (Social and Emotional Aspects of Learning) topic of 'New Beginnings', and the exploration of creation myths from other cultures. For comparison, have a look at the Aboriginal myth of the Rainbow Serpent, or read some of Rudyard Kipling's *Just So* stories together. The children could try making up their own myth about the creation of their favourite animal. You could make a collage together, adding each feature of the creation in the order in which it comes in the story to remember what happened on each day. Alternatively, you could focus on one day of creation for every day of the week, exploring topics such as light and water, planting seeds and visiting a farm or zoo.

Adam and Eve

Introduction

The story of the Fall of Adam and Eve is deceptively simple. It is, in fact, one of the most difficult stories in the Bible. Full of symbolism, and describing a time outside of the experience of any human, it leaves us with lots of questions. However, it is also one of the most important stories in the Bible, because whether it is read literally or figuratively, it is the tale that Christians use to talk about the problems of suffering and sin in the world. It is also the tale that provides the reason for all the rest. From the moment of Adam and Eve's disobedience, every story is essentially about God and his people trying to restore the relationship that was lost in Eden. The story of the Fall presents the problem that Christians believe is solved by Jesus in his death and resurrection.

Story

You will need: a bag containing figures for Adam and Eve, an apple, a snake, a fig leaf and an angel or a sword (see also *Notes for storytellers* for further ideas).

Begin by producing the story bag and explaining that the story is hiding inside. Then, bringing the objects out one by one, you might say something along these lines:

Adam and Eve: Do you remember the two people God put in the world after he had finished making it? Their names were Adam and Eve. They lived in a big garden called Eden, and they were very happy there. They didn't have to do any work, because things just grew in the garden of Eden, and they could eat any of the fruit and vegetables they found.

Apple: In the middle of the Garden of Eden there was a tree full of delicious-looking fruit. But God told Adam and Eve that the tree grew the only fruit they were not allowed to eat. In fact, if they ever touched it, they would die.

Snake: Now the snake was the craftiest of all the animals. The snake was very good at telling lies. One day the snake sidled up to Eve and asked,

'Why don't you eat the fruit on that tree?'

Eve said, 'God said we mustn't eat it. If we even touch it, we will die!'

The snake said, 'You won't die! God knows that if you eat the fruit from that tree, you will become wise, and you will know the difference between good and evil.'

Eve looked at the fruit on the tree and she saw that it looked very tasty, so she reached out her hand and took some. It tasted delicious, so she gave some to Adam, and he ate it as well.

The snake was so good at telling lies that sometimes he told the truth. You see, as they ate the fruit, Adam and Eve did know the difference between good and evil, so straight away, they knew that what they had done was very wrong.

Leaf: When Adam and Eve saw that they had done something very wrong, they hid themselves among the leaves. They were ashamed, and they didn't want God to know. But God sees everything. He came and found Adam and Eve and he was very, very angry.

Adam said, 'But Eve gave me the fruit.'

And Eve said, 'But the snake told me to eat the fruit!'

Angel: God said, 'Because you have all disobeyed me, snakes and people will always hate each other. And Adam and Eve, you won't live in this garden any more. You will have to go out into the world and work for your food.'

After they had left the garden, God put an angel with a sword at the gate so that they could never come back.

Notes for storytellers

A story bag is a simple, interactive way to present any story, especially a familiar story. The pace of the story is driven by children's curiosity about what is in the bag, and the tale is made more memorable when each part of it is represented by a visible, solid object. The objects from the bag can be offered to the children afterwards for playing through or retelling the story as a way of cementing it in their memories.

Don't be limited to the objects I used in my bag, but put in whatever you can find, especially things for the children to identify and use to guess what happens next in the story, according to the age and ability of your audience. How about a pair of binoculars to represent God looking for Adam and Eve, or a padlock to show that they could not come back into the garden?

From screen to stage

I tend not to use any kind of script at all when using a story bag: it is really only necessary to be familiar with the story and to know what each object represents. The story appears through discussion with the children, although this is almost impossible to replicate with no audience except the camera! As you bring out each object, ask a question – for example, 'What do you see?' and, 'I wonder why we have an apple in this story?'

In fairy tales, children are often very familiar with the symbols involved and can quite often tell the story to you even when they have never heard it before! Even if they have not come across this story before, you may find that they can guess that the snake will be an unfriendly character or that it isn't a good idea to eat the apple, because symbols from this ancient story have made their way into many, many others since.

Bible references

This story appears in Genesis 3.

Decoration

A tree; an apple; a snake; any of the items from the story bag.

What next?

The story of Adam and Eve's disobedience offers an explanation for sin and suffering in the world. Older children might enjoy exploring the Ancient Greek myth of Prometheus, who angered the gods by stealing fire, and Pandora, who was too curious to resist opening the box which contained evil. Compare and contrast the two stories, and then have a go at making up your own!

Noah

Introduction

Noah's ark is probably the most familiar Bible story among children. Even if they don't know the whole story, or that it comes from the Bible, they will have seen images in toys and nursery decorations, because all the animals make it a popular story to illustrate. The animals, though, take the focus off Noah and the faithful obedience which saved him from disaster.

The biblical account says that Noah found grace, or favour, in the eyes of the Lord (Genesis 6:8), but he still had to trust God's word enough to build a giant boat in the middle of dry land. For Christians, Noah's story points forwards to God's salvation of the world through Jesus, and the rainbow at the end of the story signifies God's promise, not only never to flood the world again but also to find a different way of restoring the perfect creation.

Story

You will need: a selection of musical instruments, including a keyboard or guitar, a rainstick and, if possible, a rainbow xylophone or set of rainbow bells.

When God made the world, it was good. (*Play a chord on the keyboard/guitar.*) Then Adam and Eve disobeyed God, and things started to go wrong. (*Play another chord, but add a clashing note.*) A little later on, there were people all over the earth, disobeying God. It was chaos! (*Bash random combinations of notes.*)

God wanted to start again. But there was one family, Noah's family, who had always obeyed God. So God spoke to Noah and told him to build a great big boat, because the world was about to be flooded.

Noah built a boat. Big enough for him *(use an instrument like claves or a woodblock for the sound of a hammer: tap tap)*, big enough for him and his wife *(tap tap)*, big enough for him, his wife and their sons *(tap tap)*, big enough for him, his wife, their sons, their sons' wives . . . *(tap tap tap tap)* . . . and big enough for a pair of every kind of animal in the world! *(Taptaptaptaptaptap!)*

Everyone laughed at Noah, but he finished the ark, and the animals started to climb on board. *(Here, use any instruments you have to make sounds like animals, asking the audience to suggest animals for each sound. See Notes for storytellers.)*

Then, sure enough, it started to rain *(turn the rainstick)*, and the rain went on *(turn rainstick)* and on *(turn rainstick)* and on for 40 days, until nothing could be seen of the Earth any more, and the ark was floating on top of endless water.

Eventually the rain stopped and the water started to go down. When the ark seemed to have stopped moving, Noah sent out a bird *(use a flute, recorder or whistle sound)* to have a fly around. At first the bird came back. A few days later, it came back with a branch in its beak. It had found a tree! A few days after that, the bird didn't come back. It had found enough dry land to make a nest.

Then Noah knew it was safe to open the ark. Noah, his wife, his sons, their wives and all the animals stepped outside and saw . . . *(play the rainbow instrument)* a rainbow. This was God's promise that he would look after them and never flood the Earth again.

Notes for storytellers

Any collection of musical instruments would work to make the sounds in this story. You could also use things that aren't musical instruments: pan lids, a comb and paper, teaspoons, blowing bubbles in a cup through a straw, shaking foil and plenty more imaginative combinations! Some instruments sound like animals already (a trumpeting elephant, a galloping horse) but you can be inventive with sound. Try a slow tune for a tortoise, a bouncing melody (or alternating low and high notes) for a kangaroo, and even a few recognisable tunes: how about 'Incy Wincy Spider' or the 'Teddy Bears' Picnic'? See how quickly your audience can guess the animal!

From screen to stage

With a live audience, this story could end up with plenty of participation. Children could be asked to choose an instrument, or to decide which animal each sound could represent. Alternatively, you could challenge them to find a way to make some rainstorm and animal noises using household objects or even, in a school assembly, their own bodies. Be prepared for a little bit of chaos: choose a volunteer before mentioning the noise you'd like them to make, and agree a silent signal at the beginning to restore order!

In a whole school assembly, try building the rain and flood noise by asking first one child to tap his finger on the floor in front of him, then the child sitting next to him, then the whole of that row, then add the next row back and so on. Listen to the rainstorm sound that can be made from so many little raindrop taps.

Bible references

The story of Noah and the ark can be found in Genesis 6:5–9:17.

Decoration

An ark; a rainbow; pairs of animals.

What next?

This musical method of storytelling lends itself to lots of development in an educational setting. The sounds could be developed into a performance of a sound picture, songs or an orchestral piece; or the children could be given the challenge of choosing another story to tell in the same way.

For a craft session, children could be given animals and challenged in teams to create an instrument out of junk to make a sound for that creature. Elastic bands, boxes, tins, jars and bottles of water all provide excellent beginnings for investigating sound.

Abraham

Introduction

Abraham is known as a father of the faith (or patriarch) in Judaism, Christianity and Islam. His life tells the story of the beginning of God's covenant with his people, the formation of Israel as a nation and the land that was promised to them. Abraham's direct descendants take us all the way to the end of the story of Joseph (Story 7) and his 11 brothers, who together form the 12 tribes of Israel.

Abraham is remembered for his faith, so his trust in God's promises – long before they show any sign of coming true – underpins the parts of his story told here. The story ends with the near-sacrifice of Abraham's son Isaac, which Christians believe looks forward to God's offer of his own son, Jesus, as a sacrifice for the world.

Story

> You will need: a tray of sand; three plain figures, two larger and one smaller; a piece of star-printed fabric or a picture of a starry sky. As you tell the story, move the figures as indicated in italics.

(Begin by placing the two larger figures into the tray of sand at one corner.) God called Abram out of his home to travel to a new land. 'I will make a great nation from you, and bless it, and I will make your name great,' said God. *(Draw journey tracks with your finger in the sand ahead of the two figures, then start to move the figures gradually along the tracks as you speak.)*

Abram and his wife Sarah left their home and started the journey. They travelled for a long time and had all sorts of adventures and troubles. When Abram started to lose heart, God said, 'Don't be afraid, Abram, I will make a great nation from you.'

Abram said, 'That's all very well, Lord, but I don't see your promises coming true. Sarah and I haven't had any children, so where will this great nation come from?'

But God said, 'Look down at the sand. Can you count the grains of sand?' *(Run the sand through your fingers.)*

Abram said, 'Of course not. There are far too many to count.'

God said, 'You will have children, and your children will have children, and your children's children will have children until there are more people in your family than there are grains of sand.'

And so they kept travelling, on and on wherever God led them. More adventures. More troubles. When Abram started to lose heart, God said, 'Don't be afraid, Abram, I will make a great nation from you.'

Abram said, 'That's all very well, Lord, but I don't see your promises coming true. Sarah and I haven't had any children, so where will this great nation come from?'

But God said, 'Look up at the stars. Can you count the stars?' *(Hold up the starry fabric or picture behind the tray.)*

Abram said, 'Of course not. There are far too many to count.'

God said, 'You will have children, and your children will have children, and your children's children will have children until there are more people in your family than there are stars.'

And they kept travelling.

It took a long time. It took a very long time. But God kept making the same promise. He even changed Abram's name to Abraham, which means 'Father of many people'.

Then at last, at long, long last, when they were both very old, Abraham and Sarah had a son. *(Place the Isaac figure with the other two.)* They called him Isaac, which means laughter, because they were so happy to have him.

But one day, when Isaac was a little boy, God told Abraham to do something dreadful. God said, 'Abraham, take Isaac up that mountain, and kill him as a sacrifice to me.' *(Build a 'mountain' in a corner of the tray with the sand.)*

So Abraham told Isaac that they were going on a journey to worship God, and off they went up the mountain together. *(Move figures towards the mountain.)* Isaac noticed that their donkey was carrying some wood. 'It's to make a fire for a sacrifice,' said Abraham.

'But we don't have anything to sacrifice on the fire,' said Isaac.

'God will provide something when we get there,' replied Abraham.

At the top of the mountain, Abraham tied Isaac up. *(Hold Isaac in your fist.)* He put him on top of the wood. *(Lie Isaac down on top of the mound of sand.)* He took out a knife. He raised it above his head . . . he took a deep breath . . .

'ABRAHAM! STOP!'

A voice shouted! Abraham froze, the knife in mid-air.

'Don't hurt your son, Abraham!' said God. 'You have trusted in my promises so much that you would even have given me your only son. Because of your faith in me, I promise that Isaac will grow up and have children, and his children will have children, and his children's children will have children until there are more people in your family than grains of sand, and more than the stars in the sky. And they will all be blessed because of your faith in me.'

Notes for storytellers

Some of the techniques used in telling this story are based on Godly Play, an initiative for religious education which uses Montessori methods of learning. With an emphasis on individual learning styles and independent discovery, these methods encourage children (and adults) to discover meaning in the stories for themselves. In particular, the use of symbols, blank figures and natural materials allows the watcher to project his or her own imaginings into the story. Originally developed in the United States, Godly Play has its own scripts, publications and materials; this story only borrows from some of its methods. In true Godly Play, there would be little or no eye contact between the storyteller and the audience; instead, attention is focused on the figures as the storyteller 'plays through' the story.[2]

From screen to stage

This method, of course, works best with smaller groups: everybody needs to be able to see the tray where the story is being played out, and ideally everybody would have an opportunity to handle the tray and figures themselves in a time following the telling. Because all the action happens in a small space, this method adapted well to the screen.

Bible references

The story of Abraham begins in Genesis 12, when his name is still Abram. Isaac is born in chapter 21. This story spans Abraham's life using God's promise of an heir as a refrain, but where the story says, 'They had lots of adventures', well, they really did!

If you want to look further into the story of Abraham, have a go at reading the whole thing, especially the parts about his son Ishmael who was born to a slave, Hagar, but disinherited by the birth of Isaac. Hagar and Ishmael have adventures of their own and are traditionally believed to be the founders of the Arab race. All the characters also appear in the Qu'ran.

---

2. For more about Godly Play, visit www.godlyplay.org.uk (accessed 13 May 2014).

Decoration

Stars or a photograph of a starry sky; a small jar of coloured sand; a tent; a baby.

What next?

Storytelling methods which use some form of small world play are ideal to offer as play opportunities after the telling – perhaps leaving the sand tray and props out as one of several stations for children to move around in smaller groups, exploring the story. Other stations could include the printed version of the story to read; paper and pens with a prompt to draw the most memorable scene; a photograph of the night sky with a prompt to try counting the stars; a baby name dictionary for children to find the meaning of their own names, having heard about the special meanings of Abraham and Isaac.

Sarah's name changed too, from Sarai to Sarah, which means 'princess', carrying the same implications of being at the head of a nation. Try retelling the story from Sarah's point of view, using a similar refrain structure alongside the figures and sand, but including things specific to her, such as her laughter when Isaac is promised.

Attempting to count stars and sand could provide some interesting openings for maths and science lessons: how do we measure sand?

Could there be a way of working out how many grains of sand there are in a gram? What is sand? Could we count the grains under a microscope? What do we know about the stars? How many stars are there in the Milky Way? How many stars are there that we can't see? Is it possible that the stars we see from light years away are really no longer there?

Rebekah

Introduction

When Abraham sends his slave to fetch a wife for Isaac from his own people, it is an acknowledgement that God's covenant and blessing is for Abraham's descendants and not for the people currently living in the land he is occupying. However, in the middle of all this patriarchal history is the charming story of Rebekah and of the servant who, faced with an impossible task, decides to try out his master's methods of prayer and faith. The servant, though unnamed in this passage, is referred to as 'his servant, the oldest of his house, who had charge of all that he had' (Genesis 24:2), so tradition holds that it was the previously mentioned head steward, Eliezer. The character created in this story is an example of storyteller's licence, but everything else is there in the Bible!

Story

Remember Abraham? Well, this is a story about one of Abraham's servants. We don't know his name, so we'll call him Kamir, because that's what Abraham used to say when he called him over: 'Hey! Come 'ere!'

This story happened when Abraham was very, very, very old, and his son Isaac was a young man. Isaac's mother, Sarah, had already died, and Abraham knew that his time was coming too. So he called, 'Kamir!' and Kamir came 'ere.

'Kamir, I have a very special job for you. I want you to go back to the place where I was born and find my family. I want Isaac to get married to a girl from my own country, and I want you to find her for me.'

Now, remember, Abraham had been travelling for most of his life. Kamir had a long way to go, and no idea how he might find Abraham's family, let alone a wife for Isaac, and let alone persuade her to journey all the way back with him! But he had great respect and love for his master Abraham, so off he went, with a caravan of camels loaded down with lovely presents. 1, 2, 3, 4, 5, 6, 7, 8, 9, 10 camels and one Kamir!

When he got to the right country, he found a well and sat down to have a rest. The camels all had a lie down too *(make a flopping noise after each count)*: 1, 2, 3, 4, 5, 6, 7, 8, 9, 10. They looked longingly at the cool water at the bottom of the well, but they couldn't reach it. This gave Kamir an idea.

'God of my master Abraham,' he said, 'I know you answer Abraham's prayers, so I'll try praying, too. I have no idea where to find a wife for Isaac, but here I am by this well, with ten camels, and we're all feeling thirsty. Please let Isaac's wife come here and find us. If a girl offers to give me a drink and to give all ten camels drinks as well, then I'll know she's the right one.'

As Kamir finished speaking and opened his eyes – there she was! A beautiful girl, coming towards him with a water jug.

'Hello,' said Kamir. 'Would you mind giving me a sip of water from your jug?'

'Of course,' said the lovely girl, 'and let me give your camels a drink, too.' And she poured water into a trough and went back to fetch more. She had to do it several times, until all the camels were drinking *(make a slurping noise after each count)*: 1, 2, 3, 4, 5, 6, 7, 8, 9, 10.

'What's your name?' asked Kamir.

'Rebekah,' replied the pretty girl.

'Do you live around here?'

'Yes. My dad's name is Bethuel, son of Nahor.'

Perfect! Nahor, Rebekah's grandad, was Abraham's brother!

'Any chance I could come to your house and meet your family?' asked Kamir. And so Rebekah took them all home – 1, 2, 3, 4, 5, 6, 7, 8, 9, 10 camels, and one Kamir!

Once Kamir had explained what Abraham had told him to do, Rebekah's family all looked at her. 'Do you want to go and marry Isaac?'

She looked even prettier when she was blushing. 'Yes,' she said.

So off they all went – 1, 2, 3, 4, 5, 6, 7, 8, 9, 10 camels, one Kamir, and one Rebekah in her wedding veil. Isaac came out to meet them, and it was love at first sight.

Notes for storytellers

The reference to ten camels in Genesis 24:10 is a gift to a storyteller. Any opportunity to count to ten repeatedly makes an excellent refrain for a story, especially one aimed at Key Stage 1 or below! Wonderfully, the camels really do appear all the way through the story: bemused, spitting, long-lashed onlookers. Make the most of the flopping and slurping noises. One of the advantages of counting to ten is that the children will be joining in by the end.

From screen to stage

As there are no props and a strong refrain, this story works well with any size of audience and invites plenty of participation. Encourage the children to join in with the counting, holding up their fingers each time, and to join in with the silly noises. Try counting invisible camels, putting each one in an imaginary space lined up in front of you: you will always get an extra laugh if, on the third or fourth refrain, you 'lose' the final camel and have to hunt for it, eventually 'finding' it hidden amongst the children or under a teacher's chair.

Bible references

This story appears in Genesis 24.

Decoration

Camels; a water jug; a wedding veil, rings or cake; a bride.

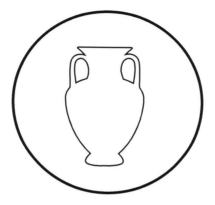

What next?

A Reception or nursery teacher could have fun with some simple addition and subtraction problems involving camels, but there is also plenty of scope in this story to look at deeper topics, such as marriage traditions in other cultures, or in traditional tales. It may seem strange to have a romantic story in which the future husband barely features, but then again, almost every child is familiar with the idea from Cinderella, Snow White or Sleeping Beauty! Older children might enjoy imagining the conversation when Isaac and Rebekah finally meet, and presenting it as a piece of writing or a script.

Jacob

Introduction

Jacob, like Abraham, is another character who receives a new, prophetic name from God, although that doesn't happen in this part of his story. His name is eventually changed to Israel, and he gives it to the nation that is fathered by his 12 sons.

In this story, we see the sly and deceitful way in which Jacob comes by his inheritance. It is a reminder that God does not choose perfect people for great things. We also hear how Jacob himself was then tricked in a rather similar way.

The vision he has of a ladder and climbing angels may not seem to have much to do with the rest of the story, but it's important to include it on the Jesse Tree because it is God's confirmation that Jacob is now next in line to continue the promise given to Abraham, of fathering a great nation. The image of the ladder between heaven and Earth is often used in Christian art to represent Jesus, especially at Christmas when we think of him as Emmanuel, 'God with us', or 'God descending to Earth'.

Story

You will need: a magic bag (see *Notes for storytellers*) and four cut-out figures, each obviously different from the rest.

Remember Isaac and Rebekah from yesterday's story? Well, they had twins! Boys called Esau and Jacob. *(As you introduce them, hold up two of the figures.)* Although they were twins, they were very different.

Esau grew up to be hairy, tough and energetic, and he enjoyed going out for days and hunting for wild animals. Jacob preferred to stay at home with his mum and his sheep and a nice cup of tea. Jacob was Rebekah's favourite son, but Isaac loved Esau. In fact, when Esau was around, it was as though Jacob didn't exist. *(Drop Jacob into one side of the bag and turn the other side inside out to show that he has disappeared.)*

Isaac was very old and blind, and he knew that he was dying. He called Esau to come and receive his blessing, as he was the eldest. But Rebekah wanted Jacob to be blessed instead. So she dressed smooth-skinned Jacob up in Esau's furry clothes, and even stuck fur to the backs of his hands and to his face so that blind old Isaac would think it was Esau's thick beard. Then she sent him in to his father. Isaac thought it was Esau. *(Drop Esau into the same side of the bag that Jacob is in, and grab Jacob.)* So Isaac gave Jacob his blessing, and only discovered his mistake later. *(Pull Jacob out of the bag.)* Wrong brother! Wrong brother! But it was too late.

Esau wanted to kill Jacob after that, so Jacob ran away.

One night, Jacob had a dream that there was a ladder reaching between heaven and Earth, with angels going up and down it, and he heard God's voice promising him all the wonderful things that Isaac had mentioned in his blessing. In particular, God promised him a very big family.

A while later, Jacob found work with a man who had two daughters. The older one was called Leah, and she had sad, tired eyes. The younger was called Rachel, and she was gorgeous. Jacob fell madly in love. In fact, when Rachel was around, it was as if Leah didn't even exist. *(Drop Leah into the bag and turn the other side inside out.)* Jacob promised to work for free for seven years if he could marry Rachel.

At last the wedding day came, and Jacob made his marriage vows to his new wife. *(Drop Rachel into the bag and grab Leah.)* But when she lifted up her veil – it was Leah! Wrong sister! Wrong sister! But it was too late. He'd been tricked! Jacob ended up having to work another seven long years so that he could marry Rachel as well.

As for God's promise of a big family, between them, Rachel and Leah had TWELVE baby boys. Twelve! But you'll have to wait until the next story to find out what happened to them.

Notes for storytellers

This story contains a magic trick. Simple illusions are a great way to catch the listeners' attention and make a story memorable, provided you are able to perform them confidently and without being distracted from the narrative while you hide something up your sleeve! In this case, all that is required is a bag with a black interior and two sections inside (I found mine in a charity shop), four foam figures in noticeably different colours, and a great deal of practice! For more Bible story friendly illusions, have a look at www.onewayuk.com.[3]

From screen to stage

Performing illusions in front of a live audience takes plenty of confidence in the technique of the trick, and it also means anticipating the scepticism of your viewers! The best thing to do is to ask for volunteers whenever this won't give the game away: for example, there are points in this trick where a child could be asked to pull the bag inside out, or to drop a figure into it, or to feel around inside and let the others know that the bag doesn't contain anything else. Of course, this necessitates checking that your props can stand up to such investigations, and also careful planning so that the volunteer is only invited to touch the bag at the right moment!

---

3. Accessed 13 May 2014.

Bible references

Jacob is born in Genesis 25:26, and the trick on Isaac takes place in chapter 27. (You may want to include – or read later – the episode in which Jacob tricks Esau into selling his birthright, in 25:29-34.) Jacob runs away in chapter 28, and his vision of a ladder takes place in 28:10-16. His marriage to Leah and Rachel takes place in Genesis 29:16-30. You may also want to read about Jacob's name changing to Israel after he wrestled with an angel, which takes place much later, in Genesis 32:22-30.

Decoration

A ladder; twins.

What next?

This is a great story for sparking a discussion about sibling rivalry and fairness! Although Esau and Jacob were twins born at almost exactly the same time, Esau came out first and should have been given the inheritance owed to the eldest son. Rebekah obviously thought this was unfair. Children often have a very strong sense of justice: do they agree with Rebekah? What would they have done if they were Jacob?

The story of Leah and Rachel is like a mirror image of Esau and Jacob. Again, it has to do with the rights of the eldest. Children will be familiar with this through fairy tales (in which, nonetheless, the youngest often ends up with the prince!). It can be interesting to pause the story after the bride turns out to be Leah. What do the children think will happen next?

Joseph

Introduction

When I was about 9 years old, everybody in my year group could sing the lyrics to *Joseph and His Technicolour Dreamcoat* from start to finish, but the children I tell the story to these days have often never heard of Joseph. It's an important tale for the Jesse Tree, not least because Joseph and his 12 brothers are the roots of the 12 tribes of Israel, and the reason for the Israelites needing to escape from Egypt. However, the story is also a great tale of forgiveness, reconciliation and restoration.

Story

> You will need: a patchwork coloured coat, with 12 patches to represent different parts of the story. Each time you see a colour in bold in the following text, add the corresponding patch to the coat. With each rhyming refrain, refer back to the coat as a reminder of the colours so far.

Jacob, Leah and Rachel had 12 sons among them. Leah had ten of those sons, and Rachel had the youngest two.

Remember how Jacob loved Rachel and had married Leah by mistake? Well, fathers shouldn't have favourite children, but Jacob did. He loved Rachel's sons best. Their names were Joseph and Benjamin, and his very favourite was Joseph. As a special present, Jacob gave Joseph a beautiful coloured coat.

Joseph started having some very strange dreams. In his dreams, he was always very important, and his 11 brothers were bowing down to him. He liked to tell his brothers all about his dreams. Not surprisingly, his brothers were **green** with envy. They were so envious that they decided to kill Joseph. They threw him into a deep, dark, **black** pit.

They would have left him there, but just at that moment, some slave traders rode past on their camels. Quickly, the brothers pulled Joseph back up out of the pit and sold him as a slave for some **silver** coins. Then they dipped his special coat in the sticky **red** blood of a goat, and they told their dad Jacob that Joseph had been eaten by a lion.

But Joseph, now on his way to Egypt, remembered his dreams: 'Green and black and silver and red; I will trust in what God said.'

In Egypt, Joseph did well, always acting honestly and working hard, and he was promoted – until his master's wife took a dislike to him and had him thrown into prison. Joseph stared out through the **grey** bars and wondered what would happen next.

There were two other people in the prison with Joseph, and they were both servants of the king of Egypt, the Pharaoh. One was Pharaoh's butler, and the other was his baker. One night, they both had strange dreams, and in the morning they told them to Joseph. The butler had a dream about making **purple** grapes into wine for Pharaoh. The baker's dream was about baking some **brown** bread which was stolen by birds.

Joseph listened and understood the dreams. He told the butler that he would be set free, and he told the poor baker that he would be put to death. He was right about both of them! The butler was let out of prison, and the baker was killed, and Joseph was left all alone again.

But it wasn't long before Pharaoh himself had a very strange dream! The butler, who was serving wine, heard Pharaoh talking about it and said, 'Hey, I met a guy in prison who can tell you what dreams mean. He understood my dream, and it came true!' So Pharaoh called for Joseph and told him all about his dream: 'I was standing by the **blue** waters of the river Nile, when 14 cows came out of the river! Seven were thin and seven were fat. Then – this is the really weird part – the seven thin cows gobbled up the seven fat ones – but they didn't get any fatter at all!'

Joseph remembered his own dreams: 'Grey and purple, brown and blue; what God promised must come true!'

'Pharaoh, your dream means that there will be seven years when the fields grow lots of food, and then there will be seven years of famine. You will need someone to organise saving up the extra food for the first seven years so that there is enough to eat during the following seven years.'

Pharaoh was so pleased that he chose Joseph to be that very important person. Joseph became Pharaoh's right-hand man, dressed in **turquoise** lapis lazuli. And during the seven years of famine, who should turn up begging for food but those 11 **stars**, Joseph's brothers! They didn't recognise him at all, but eventually Joseph revealed who he was and told his brothers that he forgave them for the way they had treated him – it was a **blank, white,** fresh start. At last, after so many years, Joseph rode out in his **gold** chariot to meet his dad Jacob, who was so very pleased to see him after so long believing he was dead.

And Joseph remembered the dreams he'd had as a boy: 'Turquoise, starry, white and gold; everything happened as God foretold.'

Notes for storytellers

Basing each section of the story on a colour for the coat is a good memory aid, both for you as you tell the story and for the children to remember it afterwards. The little rhyming refrains serve the same purpose. The story is very long and detailed, even in this abridged form. As with a story bag (see Story 2), keep the parts of the tale that go with each colour concise, and focus on Joseph's emotions rather than giving lots of dialogue.

From screen to stage

The coloured coat puzzle is designed to be interactive. In schools, I ask children to come and find the right place for each piece. The format of this story suits an episodic telling well, as the colours are there to serve as reminders and the rhyming refrains could be learned by the children. When I use it at a holiday club, the children hunt for four coloured pieces from the next episode as an opening activity. The coat then hangs in the background as a reference point during the rest of the day's discussions and activities. Told over several days, more of the abridged parts of the story could be included, especially the testing of the brothers with the silver cup in Benjamin's sack. Make sure to end each episode on a cliffhanger – there are plenty!

Bible references

Joseph's story begins in chapter 37 of Genesis and continues in chapter 39 until his death in chapter 50, although this telling finishes around chapter 46, and misses out the part about Benjamin at the end.

Decoration

Patchwork coat; hieroglyphics; Egyptian painting; Pharaoh's crown.

What next?

The story of Joseph could fit well with a topic on Ancient Egypt. The children could explore the culture that Joseph might have found himself in, finding out more about the role and lifestyle of a Pharaoh, and discovering what kind of crops were grown and what the landscape was like. They could try presenting the story as an Egyptian wall painting, or they could write Joseph's name in hieroglyphs.

Joseph's success came not only from his divinely inspired knowledge of the future, but also from his ability to come up with a solution and organise the storage and division of crops over seven years of famine. Children could find out about present-day famines, what causes them and what projects are doing to help – for example, building wells, or offering seeds or animals. They could choose a project to support and fundraise for it, or discover what else they can do to help, such as buying fairly traded goods or raising awareness.

Miriam and Moses

Introduction

Moses is such an important personality in the history of Israel that he has four stories on this Jesse Tree, and there are still so many important ones that have been left out (in particular, the story of the manna in the wilderness is really worth telling as a link to Jesus' references to the Bread of Life.) However, it's important to tell his story from the beginning because it shows two things: firstly, that Moses is in no way the archetypal hero (more of that in the next story), and secondly, that 80 years of his life before God called him were spent in preparation for his special role, although at the time he would have had no idea of the purpose of his trials. This telling emphasises the fact that, working on much bigger plans, God solved the problem without answering a single one of Miriam's desperate prayers!

Story

Joseph and his 11 brothers all ended up living in Egypt. They had children, and their children had children, and pretty soon there were loads of them. They were called the Hebrew people. The Pharaoh who had been so kind to Joseph died, and a new one took his place. This new Pharaoh woke up one morning and thought, 'Who are all these people?!'

And he panicked. He developed an immigration policy that went: 1) Make slaves of all foreigners, and 2) Kill everyone. Well, he didn't kill everyone: just all the baby boys, because he didn't want them to grow up and form an army to take over his country.

So, imagine this: Miriam is a Hebrew girl with a new baby brother, and she and her mum want to keep the baby, so they come up with a plan. They put the baby in a basket, they put a lid on the basket, and they float him down the river.

I know. It wasn't much of a plan.

Miriam stays put, hiding behind the bulrushes to see what will happen to her baby brother, and while she's there, she prays, 'God, please send help!'

Eventually someone approaches. It's the princess, the Pharaoh's daughter, who has chosen this spot to have a dip.

'Uh oh. That's not good. Normally help doesn't arrive in the shape of the enemy. OK, don't let her see the basket, please don't let her see the . . . Great, she's seen the basket. OK then, don't let her open the basket, don't let . . . Too late.' Basket open; baby crying.

But to Miriam's surprise, the princess has a look of pity on her face. 'Hello! Aren't you cute? You're one of those poor Hebrew babies that my Daddy is trying to kill, yes you are! I think I'll keep you. I'll look after you, yes I will. I'm going to call you 'Pulled-Out' because I pulled you out of the water, yes I did!'

Right then, Miriam suddenly knows what to do, and pops up out of her hiding place like a jack-in-the-box. It must have looked pretty obvious, but apparently the princess is a bit dim and doesn't stop to wonder why the reeds are sprouting Hebrew children. After all, the princess hasn't stopped to wonder how to look after a newborn baby without any milk, or realised that formula hasn't been invented yet. So Miriam asks, 'Would your Highness like a nursemaid for the baby?'

The princess lets Miriam go and find a nanny from among the Hebrew slaves, and she fetches her own mum. So mum gets paid to look after and feed her own baby. Result!

That name 'Pulled-Out' that the princess gave the baby kind of stuck. In her language it sounded a bit like 'Moses'. And it turned out to be a prophetic name, because 80 years down the line, God had a plan for old Pulled-Out and his family . . . but you'll hear more about that next time.

Notes for storytellers

This story, and the next, use a technique that I developed when I was asked to lead a holiday club for 9–14-year-olds. It's based on stand-up comedy and relies on silly asides, anachronistic references and plenty of story space.

Story space is itself a storytelling technique which involves creating an invisible 'set' full of 'props' in the space where the telling takes place. It works because the scene is also created in the imaginations of the audience: you are encouraging your listeners to project their own imaginations on to the story and make it theirs. The simple rule of story space is that although the individual objects may be visualised differently by each watcher, they always remain in the same place within the space. Once you have created an object, you will only need the direction of your gaze or the shape of your hands to refer to it again. The same is true of characters in the story: here, for example, the princess and Miriam each have their own space on the stage, and with just a few steps, the teller can indicate which one of them is speaking. For more examples of story space, look at the Notes for storytellers to Story 9.

Moses is not named Moses until the very end of the telling. His literal name, 'Pulled-Out', is important and prophetic, but that's not the only reason. When telling a familiar story to a group of older children, it's best to avoid the familiar name for as long as possible – by the time they have worked out that they recognise the story, they have already listened to most of it with much more interest and engagement than they would have done if you had told them what they were hearing at the very beginning!

From screen to stage

Story space is a technique that works much better live because you're not limited to the single viewpoint of a camera lens. By focusing your gaze beyond your audience, you can create a landscape around them: mountains or buildings behind them, people approaching from the side of them, perhaps something right in the middle of them. When telling this story in school, it's fun to visualise the bank of the river running alongside the front row of children: you can then hand the 'basket' to a child at the end of the row, encourage them all to be the water and pass the invisible basket down to the other end, where the princess can pluck the 'baby' out of the arms of one of the children. For some more examples of this, see Story 12.

Bible references

This story appears in Exodus 2:1-10 (but have a look at Exodus 1 for an explanation of Pharaoh's command).

Decoration

A basket; bulrushes; an Ancient Egyptian-style picture of the story; a baby.

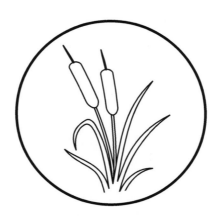

What next?

Try using this story as an opening for a science lesson! Provide the children, as individuals or in groups, with a variety of craft materials and a small baby doll, and challenge them to make a basket that can carry baby Moses safely down a washing-up basin river (or, if at home, a bathtub). The basket needs to float and be waterproof. Afterwards, they may like to look up the story in the Bible and discover the materials that Moses' mother used to achieve this!

Moses and the burning bush

Introduction

This story is wonderful because it is one of the first of many examples in the Bible of God choosing a very unlikely and imperfect human being to become a great leader. A depressed refugee with a criminal past and a set of excuses to rival a surly teenager, Moses has no idea that he is on the brink of becoming one of the most famous people in history – and one of the greatest examples of the grace and power of God.

Story

Does anyone remember the story about baby Moses in the bulrushes, who ended up being adopted by the Egyptian princess? She called him Pulled-Out because she had pulled him out of the water, and his cunning big sister found a way for him to stay with his mum until he was older.

Well, imagine we're pressing the button on the remote control to fast-forward Moses 80 years. We see Moses as a toddler being handed back to the princess who adopts him; Moses growing up in the palace, dressed like an Egyptian; Moses seeing his own people, the Hebrews, in slavery and gradually feeling more and more uncomfortable with it until eventually, he snaps. When he sees an Egyptian beating up a Hebrew and there's no one else around, he steps in, kills the Egyptian and buries the body in the sand. Now we see Moses running away,

Moses in another land marrying a foreigner, and finally Moses sitting around all day looking after his father-in-law's sheep. That's where we'll stop pressing fast forward and press play. He's probably talking to a sheep.

'Do you ever feel like you should have done something else with your life? I guess all you have to do is eat grass. But me – I've gone from Egyptian prince to sheep whisperer. What happened there?! I'm a murderer. My whole life is just pretend. I was a pretend Egyptian, and now I'm a pretend Midianite. I'm 80 years old and I've done nothing. I'm not even any good at talking to sheep – he's wandered off.'

Then something catches his attention. It's a bush that's on fire, and weirdly, it's not burning up inside the flame. Moses goes over to have a closer look, and the bush says, 'Moses! Moses!'

Now there are several ways Moses could have reacted at this point. I don't know what you would have done. I think I might have pinched myself, or at least asked the sheep whether I was hearing things. On the other hand, if Moses was the kind of person who talked to sheep, maybe it was still inside his comfort zone to be talking to shrubbery. Anyway, apparently what he said in reaction to hearing his name being called by a bush was, 'Here I am,' which I suppose was the only logical thing to say, under the circumstances.

The voice from the bush introduced itself. It said, 'I am the God of your fathers, the God of Abraham, Isaac and Jacob. I have seen the suffering of my people and the way they are enslaved by Pharaoh, but it's OK because I have a solution. It's you. You're going to go to Pharaoh and tell him to let all the Hebrews go.'

Moses said, 'Who am I to do something like that?'

God said, 'I'll be with you. It'll be fine.'

Don't forget that Moses had been an Egyptian – he barely even knew the God of his ancestors. He didn't really feel equipped to go telling other people what their own God was saying. He asked, 'What if the Hebrews test me and ask me what your name is?'

God said, 'Tell them I AM WHO I AM.'

Moses said, 'Now look. I'm currently talking to a bush which is on fire but not actually burning up, and it's talking back. Who in their right mind is going to believe me?'

God said, 'Throw that stick of yours on the ground'. Moses did, and it turned into a snake.

Moses said, 'Not helping with the believability, Lord.'

God said, 'Pick up the snake by the tail.' Moses did, and it turned back into a stick. God said, 'You can do that in front of anyone who asks, for proof'.

Moses said, 'I can do what?!'

God said, 'You can do other stuff too! For example, I can make your skin go all scabby and then heal it in front of their eyes. And if they still don't believe it, you could get some water and turn it into blood, and . . . '

Moses said, 'OK, stop with the scabs and the blood and the freaky snake trick! Look, God, the problem is – I'm rubbish. I can't speak good. I can't even string a sentence together unless I'm only talking to a sheep. I'll be like a little puddle in front of a pharaoh!'

God said, 'I made your tongue! Do you think I can't make it speak when I want to?'

Moses weighed up all these great answers to his questions and objections and then said . . . 'Please send someone else!'

At that point God got cross. 'I'm sending YOU, Moses,' he said. 'But if you really don't want to do the talking, I'll get your big brother Aaron out here to meet you. You'll have to tell him about me and what I said, but after that you can let him do all the talking.'

So that's what happened, and that's how old Pulled-Out got pulled out of hiding and ended up pulling a whole nation out of slavery.

Notes for storytellers

Like the previous story, this telling was originally created for a holiday club of 9–14-year-olds. The best way to communicate with any specific audience is to make the main character think like them, so in this story, Moses is preoccupied with questions about his identity and self-worth and talks like a teenager, despite the fact that he is 80 years old. Enjoy making him scowl and sulk, but don't make fun of him by becoming too stereotypical – your audience should want to identify with him!

Story space (see the notes for Story 8) is very important in this telling. Make sure the burning bush is planted in exactly the same place every time you refer to it, look at it or speak from it; remember where you have dropped your invisible stick so that you pick up an invisible snake from exactly the same spot. A lot depends on where you focus your gaze. When you do it effortlessly, your watchers will each see their own versions of the scene.

From screen to stage

There is a live example of this story on the website at www.kevin mayhew.com/jesse-videos. You'll notice the difference it makes to the pace, and the little extras that can be added in when everybody is laughing. There is also an example of what to do when you make a mistake! You can almost always use mistakes in your favour, especially when telling to children, for whom an adult getting it wrong is one of the funniest things in the world. Referring back to it is bound to get a laugh. For a fast-paced telling like this, improvisation is key.

Bible references

The story of the burning bush is found in Exodus 3:1–4:17.

Decoration

A burning bush; a flame; a stick turning into a snake.

What next?

This story fits well with the SEAL (Social and Emotional Aspects of Learning) topic called 'Good To Be Me'.

Discuss Moses' feelings: why did he make so many excuses? How did he feel about himself and his abilities? Then ask why God chose Moses for this special job: what has happened in his life so far that makes him the right choice? It's interesting to see how the things that Moses sees as faults and 'not fitting in' become strengths in the light of his task: he can relate to both Egyptians and Hebrews, he has a strong sense of justice and he recognises his own weakness enough to rely completely on God.

Children could take the topic further by interviewing an adult about what they do and how their lives prepared them to do it. They could then think about their own talents and experiences, what they would like to do when they grow up and how they could prepare for it (SEAL topic 'Going For Goals').

The journey

Introduction

The stories about the life of Moses would be enough to fill their very own Tree, so this poem makes brief mention of the plagues, the parting of the Red Sea and the pillars of cloud and fire that led the Israelites into the wilderness. The emphasis is on God's continuing guidance during the long journey to the Promised Land.

Story

Back when the Israelites were slaves,
God saw them in their **plight**.
Helped out by Moses and some plagues,
God's people all **took flight**.
God said to Moses, 'Don't you fret!
It's gonna be **all right**!
The sea will open up for you
so you don't have to **fight**.
I'll make a moving pillar of cloud
so keep it in your **sight**,
and then I'll make a pillar of fire
so you can walk **by night**.
Then you'll all know the way to go,
that's how I'll show my **might**.
You'll make it to the Promised Land,
led by that guiding **light**.'

Actions (to be taught first):

>**plight**: hands to head, panicked look
>**took flight**: make a flying bird shape with two hands
>**fight**: hold up fists in a boxing position by face
>**all right**: thumbs up
>**sight**: as if shading your eyes, or make a shape like binoculars
>**by night**: place hands over eyes
>**might**: hold up two fists like a weightlifter
>**light**: turn on an imaginary light with a pull switch

Notes for storytellers

This form of poetry was conceived by the brilliant storyteller Bob Hartman as a simple, memorable and effective way of telling a story. Each line of the poem is repeated three times, and each rhyme has an accompanying action. The actions are taught to the children beforehand. The rhymes and actions help the children to remember the story later, while the repetition is not only an aid to memory but also uncovers layers of meaning in the story. One way to help with this is to say the lines with a different emphasis each time.

Another of these poems appears in Story 23.

From screen to stage

This kind of poem relies on plenty of audience participation. As you repeat each line three times, making sure to include the action each time, the children will begin to join in and anticipate the rhyming words: if they are doing this enthusiastically, you can start leaving a pause before the rhyming word, perhaps just performing the action, and see how many children can remember what the word is. If you do this with a questioning look on your face, making direct eye contact, it won't look as if you have just forgotten the word!

Bible references

The first nine plagues happen in Exodus 7–10 and the tenth, the story of the Passover, happens in chapters 11 and 12. The pillars of cloud and fire appear in Exodus 13:21, and the crossing of the Red Sea takes place in Exodus 14.

Decoration

A pathway; pillars of cloud and fire; a parted sea; an arrow or signpost; a map.

What next?

This poem mentions lots of stories, all of which are worth exploring in more detail. In a school, why not have a class storytelling session, asking groups of children to research one of the stories each and to plan a way of telling, presenting or performing it to the rest of the class? Or, as a family, try having a special Passover meal, during which the story of the escape from Egypt is traditionally told.

The story is also a good starter for research and discussion about the issue of slavery, both historically and today. Listen to spirituals written by slaves, especially 'Go Down Moses', and talk about how the songwriters related their experiences to the stories of Israel's escape from Egypt and journey to the Promised Land. Have a look at anti-slavery charities such as Stop The Traffik for ideas about ending slavery today.[4]

---

4. www.stopthetraffik.org.uk (accessed 13 May 2014).

The ten commandments

Introduction

The giving of the law to Moses is an important story for the Jesse Tree because it continues the tale of God's covenant with his people that begins with Noah and goes on to the New Covenant brought about by Jesus. Surprisingly few people now know all ten commandments, so this song is a memory aid. If you are following the whole Jesse Tree, it would be worth explaining that the commandments and the law were written down and placed into the Ark of the Covenant, since that is an important feature of Story 13 (Joshua).

Story

The song goes to the tune of 'The Twelve Days of Christmas'.

There are ten commandments and they go like this, you see:
Never be jealous.
Do not lie.
Do not steal.
Stay with the one you marry.
Don't murder people.
Honour Mum and Dad!
Have a day of rest.
Respect God's name.

Don't worship idols.
There is only one God, and it's me.

Notes for storytellers

Holding up cards with the commandments written on them adds humour to the performance of the song, rather than being the best way of presenting the words. Shuffling the cards quickly enough without dropping any takes lots of planning and rehearsal! It would be just as good to have the words on an interactive whiteboard or an overhead projector, or simply to stick each card up on the wall in order and point back through them as they appear in the song. The main thing is to remember all the words and to actively encourage everyone to join in.

From screen to stage

If you are using this song in a school setting, you could ask ten children to come and hold a card each and to try to flip them up at the right moment. The song could be a fun way to finish an assembly in which you've already talked about the commandments and told the story of how they were received.

With the words displayed elsewhere, your arms would be free to add an action to each commandment. Make the performance even whackier by repeating the final verse – all ten commandments – even faster. It's fun to make a big thing of 'Honour Mum and Dad' so that the children anticipate it each time.

Bible references

The ten commandments are listed in Exodus 20.

Decoration

Stone tablets or a scroll; a list numbered 1-10.

What next?

This story is not just about the commandments themselves, but also about God's covenant with Israel. Part of the point, too, is that the commandments are difficult to keep. Christians believe that Jesus' death and resurrection were needed because nobody can manage to follow the commandments and the law all of the time! The story could be a great discussion starter about rules, why they are necessary and what to do when things go wrong. It can be very interesting to ask children to have a guess and list the ten commandments before they hear them. They often get as far as murder and stealing, but have no idea that the 'smaller' commandments such as jealousy and lying are included too, or that the first three commandments are to do with respect and love for God.

Children could have a go at writing their own commandments for use at home or at school. It's worth pointing out that Jesus, when asked which was the most important of the ten, summed up all the negative commands with two positive ones: 'Love the Lord your God,' and 'Love your neighbour as yourself' (Mark 12:28-31).

Rahab

Introduction

Rahab is an important personality on the Jesse Tree. She is one of the first outsiders to be brought into Israel, despite being a foreigner, a prostitute and a woman: a list that would have made her an outcast. Her recognition of God's power earns her three mentions in the New Testament. She appears in the list of the faithful in Hebrews; as an example of faith in action in James; and as one of four women mentioned in the genealogy of Jesus by Matthew. She is one of those Bible women who defies the stereotype by being strong willed, sharp minded and entirely in charge of her own decisions – decisions which bring her not only to be accepted into God's people, but also to become a linchpin in their history.

Story

You will need: a red ribbon, sash or belt to put on before you begin the story, to turn you into Rahab.

Yes? Can I help you?

You're not from around here, are you? I can tell by your accents. Wait a moment, you're not . . . Are you . . . Are you *Israelites*?

Well, come on in then, quickly! Don't just stand there! There are soldiers out looking for you!

Yes, I know who you are, and why you're here! We all do! The people here in Jericho have heard all about you, and we're terrified. We've heard about how your God parted the Red Sea and killed all those Egyptians, and about how he's helped you in every battle since then.

Listen, if they followed you here, they'll be here any minute. I'll help you. I will. I've heard all about you, and I believe your God is the true God of heaven and Earth. But if I help you, will you help me? Will you protect my family when you come to destroy this city? Shake on it?

Right then. Come this way. Up on the roof! Yes, it's a very useful space, isn't it? Like having another room without a ceiling. I use it to store all my equipment for making linen, so it doesn't clutter up the house. Great view, too. See over there? That's the king's palace – you're going to want to aim at that when you get in. Now, if you look this way, you'll see the River Jordan. You'll need to cross at that point over there, I expect. See how my house is part of the city wall? The city gate is round that way. Now, look over there; do you see those hills? That's where you're going to want to hide when you get out of here. I'll send the soldiers off in the other direction.

Uh oh, look! Here they come! They're in the next street! Quick, hide! Over there – get under that pile of stuff that looks like grass. Well go on, don't just stand there! I can't help it if it tickles. Just try to lie still! OK, stay there. I'm going to answer the door.

Yes? Can I help you?

You want to search the house? Why, what have I done? I'm not hiding anything. Well, come on in then – don't just stand there! Look around, you'll see there's nothing unusual. Those steps? They go up to my roof. Yes, of course you can look. See? There's nothing to see here. Just some piles of flax, drying out ready to spin into linen.

Yes, there were some men here. I have no idea who they were. I get a lot of visitors. They've gone now. They were headed towards the river. If you hurry, you'll catch them. Sorry I couldn't be more helpful.

Phew! You can come out – they've gone. Right, here's the deal. Tonight, after they've locked the gate, I'll let you through the window, down the outside of the wall and you can escape to the hills. Then – see this ribbon? I'm going to tie that in the same window. When you come back with the army, anyone inside this house is safe, OK?

You keep your side of the bargain, and I'll keep mine. I promise I won't breathe a word about you to anyone.

See you on the other side.

Notes for storytellers

Telling a story in the first person is a great way of managing lots of cultural references without having to use lengthy descriptions and explanations. Here, for example, you don't have to explain that Rahab's house would have had a flat roof, or that flax was a plant that looked a bit like grass, because they can see it all unfolding in front of them as you show them around in character.

To get into character, it's useful to have a few repeated characteristics and a repeated phrase that will keep you using the right voice and acting the part. For Rahab it's, 'Don't just stand there!', showing the way that she's taking control of the situation. It's also useful to have a physical indicator that you are going to be someone else for a while. This can be very simple: for Rahab, it's a red ribbon, sash or belt which will later become part of the story.

From screen to stage

This story was fun to film, using a moving camera to take up the position of the spies. When telling it live, the audience stays 'in character' as the spies. This means that the pile of flax needs to be imagined where the children are already sitting – because if you point to it off to one side and tell them to move under it, they probably will! So once you have 'hidden' your audience and you go to the door to let in the soldiers, keep minimal eye contact with your listeners until the 'soldiers' have gone again, and they will feel as if they have stayed hidden, watching you.

Bible references

This story can be found in Joshua 2. The New Testament mentions of Rahab (see Introduction) can be found in Matthew 1:5, Hebrews 11:31, and James 2:25.

Decoration

A red ribbon; a window; a house with a flat roof; a spy mask or looking glass.

What next?

There is lots of scope for imaginative spy-related activities to link to this story. Ask the children to create a secret message from the spies to Rahab, letting her know that they have returned safely and reminding her to take her family into her house: they will have to use a code, or hidden writing. They could try writing with lemon juice and warming it to reveal the message, or using a white wax crayon and painting watercolour black paint over the top to make the words show up. Perhaps Rahab could then send them a reply in a code for them to break – whichever linguistic or mathematical code best suits their current learning objective!

This story ends on a cliffhanger, since the children won't find out what happened to Rahab until the following tale. Challenge them to describe how they think the battle of Jericho went, and then play them the next video or tell the next story to see if they're right. Alternatively, they could watch both stories and then recount the Battle of Jericho from Rahab's point of view, using her voice and character to kickstart their own writing, storytelling or acting.

Joshua

Introduction

Joshua was a warrior and a leader who had the unenviable task of coming after Moses. It's not easy to stand in the place of someone who has been seen communicating directly with God, calling down plagues and parting seas. Joshua's way of making his own mark was simply to stick unswervingly and fiercely to the word of God and the law.

The Ark of the Covenant containing the ten commandments and the rest of the law is at the very centre of this story, placed by Joshua at the head of the army as a constant reminder that any victory will come from God.

Story

You will need: figures to represent Joshua, Rahab and the angel; a group of figures to represent the army; bricks to build the walls of Jericho; a special-looking box for the Ark of the Covenant; fabric or paper to be the River Jordan. This tale uses simple small world play: as you tell it, set out the scene and move the figures through the story.

Remember meeting Rahab in the last story? Well, after Rahab helped the two spies to escape, they reported back to their leader. Moses had died, and the man leading the Israelites now was called Joshua. After 40 years in the wilderness, they were finally about to make it into the Promised Land. Jericho – where Rahab lived – was the first city they would have to conquer.

There were two problems. First, they had to cross the River Jordan, which was a deep, wide, fast-flowing river with no bridge. Secondly, the city of Jericho itself had a strong, thick wall all the way around it.

Joshua was a wise and faithful man, and he knew that if one thing was going to carry them through, it would be making sure they were following God's word and God's instructions. Joshua actually had God's words and instructions, because Moses had written them down, and they were kept in a special box called the Ark of the Covenant. Joshua arranged for the priests carrying the Ark of the Covenant to go down ahead of the people and wade into the river. As soon as their feet touched the water, the river parted, just like the Red Sea had done for Moses. Job done. The Israelites, armed and ready for battle, passed through and their families followed. The whole time they were crossing, the priests and the Ark stood still in the middle of the river bed. Only when everyone had crossed did the priests follow, and then – crash! – the water fell back into place.

Now they were camped opposite Jericho, which was walled up like a fortress. Joshua knew that the only way to get in would be to follow God's word and God's instructions. But he wasn't sure what God's instructions were, so he waited. Eventually an angel arrived and explained what they should do.

If I'd been Joshua, I think I might have lost my nerve at this point. But he didn't. Unlike Moses, he didn't seem to mind when God asked him to do something that sounded utterly crazy. Once again, he put the priests carrying God's word at the front of the army, and they started to march around the wall. The priests also had horns, which they were blowing the whole time. All the way round they went – then they went back to their camp. The people inside the walls must have wondered what on earth was going on. And they couldn't believe it when the next day, Joshua and his priests and his army got up and did exactly the same thing again! All the way round the walls once, blowing the horns, and then back to the camp. This went on for six days!

On the seventh day, up they got and walked around the city again, but this time they kept going. Once round. Twice round. Three, four, five, six and seven times. Then Joshua said, 'Now, make a noise!' So everybody shouted and blew on their trumpets – and suddenly, the walls of Jericho crumbled.

Afterwards, when the battle was won, Joshua sat all the people down around the Ark of the Covenant – everyone, from the oldest grandparents to the youngest children – and read the whole of God's word to them, every word that Moses had ever written down. He wanted to be sure that they remembered what had won them the victory. And sitting with them was Rahab, who had been rescued just as the spies promised. With her family, she joined God's people and listened to the stories from long ago.

Notes for storytellers

Using small world play as part of storytelling is a great way to help children to imagine the scene and to encourage them to extend the story in their own imaginations through play later on. Though this is similar to the reflective storytelling style found in Story 4, small world play can be more colourful, more interactive and closer to the way in which small children actually play, using found objects to become props and putting the characters through the motions. The film for this story used blank wooden figures and coloured bricks as well as bits of fabric, but it would be just as appropriate to borrow your children's building bricks, or anything else which invites them to join in the play.

From screen to stage

If you are telling this story to a larger group of children, there's no need to be limited to little bricks and figures. Why not act it out on a grand scale with stacking boxes, armchair cushions and blankets, and let the children themselves act as the army? You could also add real musical wind instruments to make the trumpet noises. Whatever you use, though, make sure you have something that looks really special to be the Ark of the Covenant – the most important prop in the story.

Bible references

The story is found in the Book of Joshua. Joshua parts the River Jordan in chapter 3, sees the angel in 5:13–6:5, captures Jericho in chapter 6 and reads the law to all the people in 8:30-35.

Decoration

A trumpet; the Ark of the Covenant or a scroll; a broken wall.

What next?

Why not listen to or learn to sing 'Joshua fit the battle of Jericho'? There are many different versions – some fast and rhythmic, some slow and contemplative, some with verses and some without. In the best storyteller tradition, this spiritual song has been changed about and turned inside out through being passed down by word of mouth since the early nineteenth century, when it was probably written by slaves. Children could use the chorus and have a go at writing their own verses to tell the story.

Ruth

Introduction

Ruth is one of only two women to have a whole book of the Bible devoted to her story. She is remembered for her loyalty to her mother-in-law, Naomi, when, after losing her husband, Ruth makes the countercultural choice to travel to Naomi's homeland rather than stay in her own country to marry again. Her marriage to Boaz, son of Rahab, means that like her mother-in-law, she is another foreigner brought into Israel and added to the genealogy of Jesus. The reference to Royal David's City at the end is the first moment on the Jesse Tree which points directly towards Christmas.

Story

You will need: a basket and large piece of cloth or a shawl.

This is a story about family, and Naomi had none left. Her husband and both her sons had died, and Naomi was left with two daughters-in-law, Orpah and Ruth. *(Here, the basket becomes a grave or coffin, with the shawl draped over the top.)*

This is a story about family, and Ruth didn't want another one. She wanted to stay with Naomi, her beloved mother-in-law, the only link left to her lost husband.

This is a story about family, and Naomi's family lived in a town called Bethlehem. So the two women packed their bags and set off. *(As you say this, fold up the cloth and pack it into the basket.)* When they arrived, it was the beginning of the barley harvest, so Ruth decided to go into the fields, where poorer people were allowed to follow the harvesters around and pick up any grain they dropped. She happened to choose a field belonging to a man named Boaz. *(While Ruth is harvesting grain, pick up imaginary grain from the ground and place it into the basket as you talk.)*

This is a story about family, and Boaz had some important family connections. For a start, he was the son of Rahab – remember her? – the woman who had looked after the Israelite spies, and who became a part of God's people when the walls of Jericho fell? Secondly, and even more importantly for this story, Boaz was related to Naomi's late husband. So when he heard who Ruth was and what she had done for Naomi, he developed a soft spot for her. He invited her to stay in his field, and he whispered to his workers that they should pull out some bits of grain and drop them on purpose so that Ruth would pick up extra. And at lunchtime, he invited her over to share his picnic. *(Spread out the cloth like a picnic blanket and sit on it.)* So every day until the end of the harvest, Ruth went back and worked in Boaz's field.

This is a story about family, and Naomi knew that it was time for Ruth to think about starting one. And who better for Ruth than a kindly man like Boaz? But Naomi knew something else, something that would clinch it. On the night of the end-of-harvest party, she told Ruth to have a bath, put on some perfume and wear her best dress. *(Get dressed by draping the cloth over your shoulders or around your waist.)* Then she sent Ruth to the party with a special message for Boaz. Ruth waited until everyone was falling asleep, and then she went and curled up next to Boaz. In the middle of the night, Boaz woke up with a start and wondered why there was a woman in his bed!

'Who are you?'

'It's Ruth. Did you know that you are the one with the right to marry me – the closest relation to my late husband?'

Boaz chuckled. 'Well, well! And when you could have had your pick of all the young men, too! I would love to grant your request,

Ruth, but actually there's a closer relation than me, and he has the right to marry you. But stay where you are – I'll sort it out in the morning.'

This is a story about family, and family can be awkward. Boaz had to act very carefully. The next morning he called over the man who had the right to marry Ruth and said casually, 'Naomi is selling her husband's field, and you have the right to buy it. I'm next in line after you. Do you want it?'

'Sounds good to me,' said the man.

'Oh, by the way, the field comes with a wife,' said Boaz. 'Naomi's daughter-in-law, Ruth.'

'In that case, I can't! I'd spoil my own inheritance. You go ahead and take the field, and the girl.' *(Have a moment for Ruth and Boaz to get married – place the cloth over your head like a veil.)*

This is a story about family, and before long Boaz and Ruth made a new one. Naomi was soon a proud grandma to a little boy called Obed, and everybody said she looked young and happy again. *(Obed is the cloth bundled up like a baby, placed into the basket and rocked.)*

This is a story about family. God's family. You see, Obed had a son called Jesse, and Jesse had a son called David, and David became king, which is why Naomi's home town became known as Royal David's City. And 'Once in Royal David's City . . . ' well, do you know the rest?

Notes for storytellers

This lovely story can be quite long and complicated for children to understand, especially given that so much of it is grounded in the social rules of an unfamiliar culture. For this reason, I chose the refrain about family, which holds the story together on a familiar theme. Refrains give a rhythm to a story and make it more memorable for the audience to retell later.

This story also has a visual refrain in the form of Ruth's basket. It becomes a suitcase to pack her clothes when she travels with Naomi, a container for the grain she gathers and a cradle for her new baby. Using a single prop in several ways like this encourages the children to use their imaginations, both as they listen to the story and in their own play as everyday objects can become any number of different things. It also gives them an object to associate with the character: why not hang a little basket on the Jesse Tree?

From screen to stage

This story really needs no adaptation, and suits small and large audiences equally. Where there is dialogue, remember that a slight turn of your body followed by a look towards the space you were standing in a moment ago shows the change of speaker without the need for clunky 'he said, she said' moments. Take your time using the props: the physical refrain is important, and the audience will need a moment to see what the basket has become each time.

Some of the actions involved here, like putting on the cloth as a wedding veil, work best with a female storyteller. If you are a man telling this story, you could consider asking a child to volunteer to come and use the props instead.

Bible references

The whole book of Ruth is devoted to this story. You may also find Micah 5:2 useful, as this is the first mention of the family that comes from Bethlehem.

Decoration

A basket; a sheaf of wheat; clasped hands; two women hugging.

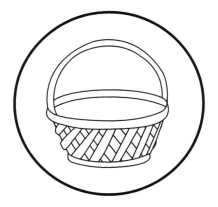

What next?

Ruth is the perfect story to prompt thinking about family, home and belonging, matching the SEAL themes 'New Beginnings', 'Good to Be Me', 'Relationships' and 'Changes'. Children could have a go at making their own family trees, bringing in photographs of their relations and talking about their homes – especially if they have come from different countries and cultures. Floella Benjamin's autobiographical book *Coming to England* would be a good way to extend this theme.

Ruth's song to Naomi (Ruth 1:16, 17) has been set to music by several composers and is often sung at weddings. One such setting is 'Wherever You Go', by the Monks of Weston Priory.

Samuel

Introduction

The story of Samuel's calling is a very popular one to tell to children, not only because Samuel is a child himself in the story, but also because of that set of three calls and replies as well as the humour of waking old Eli up three times, all of which has storytellers and children's writers rubbing their hands in glee. However, children's adaptations of the tale often leave out the tricky part of the message that Samuel is actually given when he replies to God's call. Of course it's difficult to explain exactly what Eli's sons have been doing wrong, but you don't have to: the point is that it's not good news, and Samuel bravely passes on the message anyway.

Samuel is the first of a little group of prophets whose lives and messages are explored on the Jesse Tree. None of the prophets had a very easy time, and Samuel was no exception.

Story

In this story, ask the children to respond 'Here I am!' every time they hear the words 'Samuel! Samuel!'

At first, Eli looked after Samuel. Samuel was only a little boy, growing up in the temple without his family. Eli, the old priest, was like a father and a grandfather and a teacher all at once, looking after Samuel, teaching him how to do his work in the temple, telling him stories about God.

But recently, Samuel had been looking after Eli. Poor old Eli was doddery on his feet and he was going blind. He needed help up the steps and help around the temple as he went about his work. Every now and then, Eli would get stuck doing something, and he would call out, 'Samuel! Samuel!'

'Here I am!' Samuel would call, and come running.

One night, Samuel was asleep in his place in the temple, when he heard, 'Samuel! Samuel!'

'Here I am!' he answered, and hurried to Eli's bed. But Eli was asleep – or at least, he was until Samuel came crashing into the room!

'I didn't call you! Go back to bed!' said Eli gruffly.

So Samuel went back to bed, but just as he was drifting off to sleep he heard, 'Samuel! Samuel!'

'Here I am!' he yelled, and ran to Eli's bed. But Eli was asleep again – or at least, he was until Samuel came crashing into the room!

'I didn't call you. Go to sleep!' yawned Eli.

So Samuel went back to bed, but just as he was drifting off he heard, 'Samuel! Samuel!'

'Here I am!' called Samuel, and he ran to Eli's bed, but Eli . . . well, you've guessed it, haven't you?

'I didn't call you, but perhaps God is trying to call you. If you hear the voice again, say, 'Here I am, Lord; your servant is listening', suggested Eli.

So Samuel went back to bed, full of wonder. There were no prophets who were hearing from God in those days, and it had been many long years since anybody had received a vision from God, though Samuel knew all about them from the stories Eli told. Samuel got back into bed feeling quite excited, and tried to stay awake this time! At last he heard, 'Samuel! Samuel!'

'Here I am!' shouted Samuel, and then remembered, 'Your servant is listening!'

And God spoke to Samuel. But God did not have very good news to give to Samuel. In fact, he had a terrible, horrible message to give him. God told Samuel that Eli's sons, who were both priests like Eli, had been doing dreadful things instead of serving God. Not only that, but Samuel had to tell Eli that his sons were going to die.

In the morning, Samuel heard Eli calling, 'Samuel! Samuel!'

'Here I am!' replied Samuel, and slowly he got up and went to find Eli – poor, old, blind, doddery Eli who had been so kind to him.

What do you think Samuel should do? Would you give Eli the bad news?

It was the hardest thing Samuel had ever had to do, but he obeyed God. He sat Eli down and told him as gently as he could what God had said to him. Eli sat quietly, listened, and then said, 'God's will be done.'

As for Samuel, because he listened to God even when it was very difficult, he went on to be one of God's greatest prophets. He even anointed kings, and if you listen carefully, you might hear him turning up in the next story, when he's much older!

And every time Samuel heard God calling, 'Samuel! Samuel!'

'Here I am!'

Notes for storytellers

Whenever there is repetition in a story (and in storytelling, there very often is), try to keep every repeat as similar as possible in your wording, tone of voice, actions and position on the stage. Doing so helps the audience to anticipate the repeat, which both adds to the humour and creates a bigger surprise when the repetition is finally broken.

Similarly, when introducing the refrain, make sure that you always call, 'Samuel! Samuel!' in the same tone of voice so that the children don't respond every time you say his name in the story. It can help to add an action, too.

From screen to stage

There's an opportunity in this story to gather the children's opinions: 'What do you think Samuel should do? Would you give Eli the bad news?' This could be an opportunity to put a real break in the story and explore the options with group discussion, a conscience tunnel or a writing activity (see *What next?*).

Bible references

The story appears in 1 Samuel 3.

Decoration

An ear; a bed; a telephone.

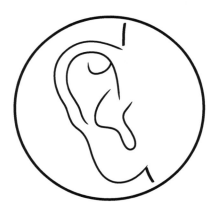

What next?

This story is a good starter for discussions about listening and communication, as well as prayer. Samuel's name means 'God hears' because he was an answer to his mother's prayer (1 Samuel 1:20). Try playing a game in which somebody is blindfolded and guided around obstacles by listening to a friend's voice.

Once Samuel has heard the message, he has to pass it on. This can be a good basis for talking about words, how some things are hard to say and how our words affect other people. For older children, give out cards printed with tasks – ranging from 'feed the cat' to 'fly a plane' – and ask them to put the tasks in order of difficulty, beginning with 'easy' and ending with 'impossible'. In the set, include several things that are spoken, such as, 'Say the alphabet,' 'Tell someone you love them,' or 'Order a coffee.' Also include, 'Tell someone that their son has died.'

When the children have finished discussing and sorting the cards together, ask them why they placed this last one where they did. Play devil's advocate a bit to get them discussing – for example, 'Why is it harder than saying the alphabet? After all, you're only saying one sentence to somebody!' You could also expand on it to see if the children might move it: 'Would it be easier if you didn't know the person? Would it be harder if you knew the person who had died? Where would you put it if it was your fault they had died?'

Jesse's sons

Introduction

So many children's stories show the small triumphing over the great, and the childhood stories of King David shine with that quality. Even before the more popular tale of David and Goliath (Story 17), God's choice of David over all his big brothers is an enjoyable boost for the confidence of small children. David hasn't even been included in the line-up: he's looking after the sheep. Children identify with the feeling of being overlooked or told they are too small to join in, so they can readily put themselves in David's shoes and share his triumph.

Story

> You will need: a Russian doll or equivalent toy – for example, you could use stacking cups. Alternatively, just put eight teddies or dolls of varying sizes into a bag.

Do you remember Samuel, from yesterday? Remember how he grew up to become a prophet and pass on lots of messages from God? Well, when he was much older, God had another really difficult job for him to do.

God said, 'Samuel, I want you to go and anoint a new king over Israel.'

Samuel said, 'Hang on a minute, God. There is already a king over Israel. His name is Saul, and he's really rather powerful. If I try choosing somebody else to be king, he'll probably kill me.'

I said it was a difficult job, didn't I? But Samuel, being Samuel, obeyed God all the same. God sent him to a man called Jesse – do you recognise that name? Jesse had eight sons, and God explained that one of Jesse's sons would be the new king.

Jesse lined up all his sons – all but the youngest.

(Produce the Russian doll, and each time a new son is talked about, open up the doll to reveal another smaller one.)

The eldest son was very strong, and very handsome. Samuel thought he would make a great king. But then he heard God say, 'No, he's not the one.'

The next son was also very strong, and very handsome . . . *(Repeat until the seventh doll, getting faster as you go.)*

Samuel asked Jesse whether he had any more sons, and Jesse brought in David, his youngest son, who was still only a boy and had been out in the fields looking after the sheep. He was small and a bit puny and probably smelt of sheep, but God said, 'That's him!' So Samuel anointed him king by pouring oil over his head.

Of course, David didn't get to go and be king straight away. There was still a king on the throne, remember? David had quite a few encounters with that king, and you'll hear about the first of them in the next tale from the Jesse Tree.

Notes for storytellers

The bulk of this story is repetition, so it's an easy one to learn! Say the refrain slightly faster each time, varying it so that as you go along it loses a few words as well. ('The next son was also strong and handsome, and Samuel thought, 'Great!' But God said 'He's not the one.') The audience will get caught up in the pace, and so much repetition always gets younger children giggling. Make sure there is plenty of contrast when David finally arrives on the scene: slow everything down again as you describe him.

From screen to stage

When telling this story to eight or more people, ask them to be the brothers, in order of size. Bring each volunteer to the front to show you their muscles (for 'strong') and strike a pose (for 'handsome'). Then get them to stick out their bottom lip to show how disappointed they are not to be chosen, and stomp back to their seats. This can be hilarious by the time you get to the fourth or fifth brother, because the volunteers are emboldened by the people who have gone before them and the actions get progressively bigger and sillier!

When it comes to David, try to choose the tiniest member of the audience, especially if you have previously ignored their waving hand – they relish the feeling of a second chance. The last time I told this story, I chose a baby who had come to church to be baptised. It made the point perfectly: God chooses little people for great futures.

Bible references

This story takes place in 1 Samuel 16:1-13.

Decoration

A crown; a jar of oil; a child.

What next?

There are so many stories in the Bible about people who seem weak or small on the outside being chosen by God. A verse from this story says that 'Mortals . . . look on the outward appearance, but the Lord looks on the heart' (1 Samuel 16:7). The verse has been made into a fun action song by John Hardwick.[5]

Jesus told a story with a similar theme about a mustard seed which grows into the biggest tree (Matthew 13:31-32). Explore small beginnings with your children by looking at seeds and trying to guess which plant they will grow into. Investigate other examples of surprising strength in the natural world, such as fleas jumping to 150 times their own height, and ants carrying hundreds of times their own weight.

---

5. *Bible Bop Workshop* CD and DVD, John Hardwick, track 2 (Kingsway).

David and Goliath

Introduction

The story of David and Goliath has all the ingredients for a very popular tale with children: the fairytale excitement of a giant, the vocabulary of swords and armour and battle, and not least the triumph of the small boy after everybody has laughed at him. In fact, it's easy to get carried away and forget the most important part of the story: that David wins because of his faith in God. He is not like a Brer Rabbit of folk tales, overcoming the bigger opponent through trickery or 'brains over brawn': instead, he knows that he has to rely on God's help.

Story

You will need: one large balloon, one permanent marker pen, a pin and a balloon pump – or a lot of puff! Every time somebody talks about how big Goliath is, blow up the balloon a bit more. I've marked the likely places with the word 'Balloon'.

Remember little David, who was anointed as king by Samuel? Well, after that, life pretty much went back to normal. More being the littlest. More looking after sheep. His three eldest brothers went and joined the army. They were fighting a war against a people called the Philistines. Little David was a bit jealous. He quite enjoyed going up to the camp and hanging out with his brothers, imagining what it would be like to be a real live soldier like them.

One day, David was taking some packed lunch to his brothers in the camp, and he found them looking very worried indeed. They explained that one of the Philistines was coming out every morning and challenging any soldier to single combat. The winner, he said, would win the entire war.

'Well, why doesn't someone go ahead and fight him, then?' asked David. 'Then we could win the war and you three could come home.'

'David, you're cute but you're not very bright,' said his eldest brother.

'You don't get it,' said his next brother. 'This guy – his name's Goliath – well, he's BIG. I mean, he's really big!' *(Balloon.)*

'In fact, he's a GIANT!' said David's third brother. *(Balloon.)*

Before they could say anything else, Goliath himself came into view on the horizon and began to shout out his challenge again. And wow, was he big! *(Balloon.)* He was enormous! *(Balloon.)* All dressed in bronze armour that must have weighed the same as a small house. *(Balloon.)*

'I'll fight him,' said David. His brothers fell about laughing. But David set off to see King Saul.

King Saul fell about laughing too. 'You?! You're just a kid! And Goliath is huge! *(Balloon.)* You'd fit inside his pocket! You're probably about the size of one of his boots!'

David said, 'Look, I'm a shepherd, and while I'm looking after my dad's sheep, I sometimes have to kill the odd lion or bear. I can manage them all right. Besides, God is on our side.'

King Saul was impressed by the lion-killing part. 'All right' he said. He gave David his own armour to fight in. David was so small that when he put it on, he could hardly see out. He tried to lift up the sword. He couldn't. So he took it all off again.

'All I need to defend me is God,' he said, 'and my shepherd's sling – the one I made myself.'

So he picked up some smooth stones from the river and wandered over to meet Goliath.

Goliath was even bigger close up *(balloon)*, and he had a loud, mean laugh *(balloon)* and a nasty expression on his face. *(Draw a face* on the balloon. *As you put the pen down, secretly pick up the pin.)* He shouted a few rude words at David, but David did the fighting talk better. 'You have armour and a sword and a javelin, but I have the power of God!' he yelled, 'and I'm going to kill you and cut off your head with your own sword!' Then he whirled his sling up over his head and let loose a single stone. It flew through the air and . . . *(Pop the balloon!)*

Goliath was struck between the eyes and toppled to the ground. David wandered over, picked up the enormous sword (it took both hands and a lot of effort) and cut off his head.

And that was that.

Notes for storytellers

This story has the focus of the balloon to keep the audience engaged, but there is plenty more you can do with it. Don't miss the contrast between David's high-pitched, tiny voice and Goliath's booming one, and all the humour there is to be had in David's piping death threats – the smaller you can make his voice sound, the funnier it is.

From screen to stage

Some children are very afraid of loud bangs, and often when I tell this one in a school the children in the front two rows all have their hands over their ears as soon as I produce the balloon. So instead of popping it, at the crucial moment I let it go and it flies around the hall. This gets a big laugh, and can then be followed by wandering over to pick up the deflated 'head' and carrying it back to King Saul, held between finger and thumb at arm's length!

Bible references

The story is found in 1 Samuel:17.

Decoration

A slingshot; five stones; a helmet or sword; a giant figure next to a tiny one.

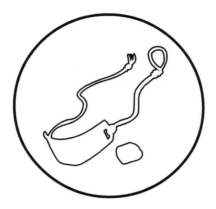

What next?

This story has inspired some enjoyable songs for children, especially 'Goliath Was a Mighty Man' by Joseph Martin, and 'Only a Boy Named David' by Arthur S. Arnott.

This could be a fun story to continue in a PE lesson with some target practice: soft balls to be thrown at a 'Goliath' target stuck to a wall!

Older children might like to find out about more recent acts of faith and bravery from people such as Nelson Mandela, William Wilberforce, Corrie Ten Boom or David Wilkerson. All these people, and many more, stood firm in their faith in God against an enormous enemy and achieved great things.

David writes a song

Introduction

Nobody knows when David wrote his best loved psalm: Psalm 23, the one about the Good Shepherd, which has been set to music and recited and learnt by rote for thousands of years. Some guess that it was near the beginning of his life; others that it was after that difficult patch with Bathsheba; still others say there is no evidence that he wrote it at all. However, weaving a psalm into a story is a great way to present it to a younger audience, so here, the comforting psalm – about being a shepherd, and being a king – is composed by David to soothe King Saul during his depressions. Why not?

Story

Do you remember little David, who killed the giant? Well, after he had killed Goliath, David *still* didn't get to be king. But he did get to go and live in the palace. King Saul made him his armour-bearer until he was old enough to join the army.

Now King Saul was not quite well in his mind. He had long times of depression, black moods and fierce rages. During these times he wouldn't let anyone near him, and went scowling around the palace, refusing to engage in any affairs of state. Nobody quite knew what to do about it.

One day, somebody suggested that music might help. Somebody else said, 'David plays the lyre. He's quite good. Send him in to the king.' So David, rather nervously, picked up his lyre and in he went.

Wondering what might help, he made up a song about what he knew: being a shepherd, following God, being a king.

> God is like a shepherd
> and I am like his sheep,
> he leads me out to eat and drink,
> he brings me home to sleep;
> he shows me the right way to go,
> so I will have no fear
> and even in my darkest times he's near.

> My enemies can see
> how he looks after me,
> he anointed me with oil, just like a king;
> his goodness and his mercy
> will follow me for ever
> and all my life I know that I will sing.

> God is like a shepherd
> and I am like his sheep,
> he leads me out to eat and drink,
> he brings me home to sleep;
> he shows me the right way to go,
> so I will have no fear
> and even in my darkest times he's near.

The song comforted Saul, and it's been comforting people ever since. David wrote lots more, and he kept writing them even when eventually, a lot later, he did get to become king himself. In fact, lots of people still love to sing and pray with David's songs. You can read most of them for yourself in the Book of Psalms.

Notes for storytellers

This is a very simple story to tell, and very short. On the video, the little aside about my ukulele looking nothing like a lyre would work for any instrument you choose to use – or none! If you prefer to play the song from the website, you could joke that a lyre was a very early form of iPod . . . The track is available at www.kevinmayhew.com/jesse-videos.

From screen to stage

Why not teach the song and have everyone joining in for the second time? The backing track is available at www.kevinmayhew.com/jesse-videos.

Bible references

David's song is taken from Psalm 23. The rest of the story takes place in 1 Samuel 16:14-23.

In the New Testament, Jesus uses the same imagery when he refers to himself as the good shepherd (John 10:1-16) and tells the parable of the lost sheep (Luke 15:3-7).

Decoration

A lyre; musical notes or a treble clef; a sheep.

What next?

This is the only psalm on the Jesse Tree, so the children could have a look at some other psalms to get an idea of their subjects and the way they were written. They could have a go at writing a psalm or a song of their own based on Psalm 23, listing examples of what God does for us. In fact, a teacher could stop halfway through telling the story and ask the children to get involved in it by helping David to write a song that might soothe King Saul.

Younger children might enjoy focusing more on sheep and shepherds, finding out what a shepherd does to take care of his sheep and getting stuck in to some cotton wool ball sheep-related crafting. Have a look at the Bible references to find Jesus' reference to himself as the good shepherd, and the story of the lost sheep.

Elijah

Introduction

Elijah was a prophet who was so important in Israel's history and so linked to messianic belief that Jesus' disciples were expecting him to reappear before the Messiah. Some people thought that Jesus was, in fact, Elijah (Matthew 16:14). At the transfiguration, it was Moses and Elijah who showed up to talk to Jesus (Matthew 17).

Moses and Elijah share a similarity in that God allowed them both to have a level of control over the natural world that was only surpassed by Jesus. This story, in which Elijah's prayers can control the rain and the fire, is a great example of this.

Story

This story begins when God's people were in a real mess. It was long after the time of King David; the kingdom had split into two and there were two different kings. And all of God's people had long since forgotten his commandments. They were breaking every single one of them, especially the first two – do you know what the first two commandments were? They were worshipping another God called Baal.

God sent a prophet called Elijah to sort them all out. As well as that, God stopped the rain. When our story starts, there had been no rain for nearly three years. There was drought and there was famine. The king, whose name was Ahab, was getting really fed up. So Elijah went to Ahab and said, 'There's only one way God will bring the rain back, and that's if everybody turns back to him.'

Elijah could tell from Ahab's face that he wasn't going to get anywhere, so he said, 'Let's try a little experiment and sort this out once and for all. Look at me: I'm the only prophet God has left, but Baal has 450 priests, so I think this will be a fair experiment. Come up to the top of Mount Carmel with me, bring everybody with you, and we'll see what we will see.'

So at the top of the mountain, Elijah had two altars set up – one for the priests of Baal and one for himself. On each of the altars he put a freshly slaughtered bull, and then he said to the priests of Baal, 'Right! Your turn first! See if your god, Baal, will send some fire to consume the sacrifice on his altar.'

So the priests of Baal started to walk round and round their altar, singing songs, praying and chanting strange chants. Elijah sat and watched them going round and round and round. It went on for hours! By the time it got to midday, Elijah was beginning to enjoy himself. He said, 'Go on, shout louder! I'm sure Baal's up there somewhere! He'll hear you eventually. Maybe he's just nipped into town. Or perhaps he's reading a book. I bet he's on the toilet! Shout louder and he'll hear you!'

And they did shout louder. They were shouting and crying and screaming and singing, and some of them even started to cut themselves with knives – what a spectacle! Elijah let it go on for about another hour, and then he'd had enough.

'All right,' he said. 'That's enough of that. My turn.' Elijah got up and went across to his altar. He said, 'Bring me some pots of water.' So they did, and he poured them over and around the altar, soaking the wood and the sacrifice on top. Then he knelt down and he said one short, quiet prayer. There was a moment of silence. Then, whoosh! The whole thing went up in flames, out of nowhere! When the flames had died down, there was nothing left. Not the bull, not the wood, not the water, not even the stones that the altar had been made from. Everything was turned to ash.

Elijah didn't need to say anything else to make his point. All the people fell on their faces and started worshipping God straight away.

Ahab wasn't so sure. He said to Elijah, 'Pff. You still haven't made it rain.' Elijah looked up into the sky and saw a little cloud coming in over the sea, and he smiled to himself. 'I think you'd better get back to the palace,' he told the king. Well, Ahab leapt into his chariot and raced back to the palace, but he didn't make it in time. He was soaked by the most enormous rainstorm the country had ever seen. Everybody else ran home to watch from inside as the rain poured down onto the parched earth for the first time in three years. But if you had stayed outside, you would have seen one little figure running down the mountainside with his skirts up around his knees, chortling to himself. It was Elijah.

Notes for storytellers

Some accounts in the Bible are so visual, so full of life and so brilliant in their dialogue that it really only remains to tell them, and this is one of those. Elijah's mocking of the priests of Baal genuinely does contain a reference to the toilet, and what more could you want to provoke hilarity in children? The most important technique used here is story space (see the notes to Stories 8 and 9): place each of the altars somewhere in your imagination and use your hands and eyes to bring the scene to life.

From screen to stage

There is plenty that audiences can do to join in with this story: try making up a chant (it could be just nonsense words, with silly actions) for the priests of Baal to sing and have them perform it between each of Elijah's taunts, becoming louder and sillier with every repetition. There is also a fun way to build the sound of a torrential rainstorm at the end of the story (see the *From screen to stage* section of Story 3, Noah).

Bible references

This story comes from 1 Kings 18.

Decoration

Flames; a raincloud; two altars.

What next?

The long drought at the centre of this story (and other stories about Elijah in 1 Kings 17) provides an ideal opportunity to look at the theme of water: anything from learning about the water cycle to investigating the essential part that water plays in life. Children could keep a journal of every time they run a tap or use water during the day; they could measure rainfall over a few weeks and compare their results to rainfall statistics here and in other countries; or they could look into the work of a charity such as Water Aid and think about what they can do to help people who have little water, or dirty water.[6]

Jesus referred to himself as 'living water' or 'the water of life' (John 4:10-13; John 7:37). After their investigations, the children could consider what that image means, perhaps producing some artwork or creative writing on the theme.

---

6. See http://www.wateraid.org/uk (accessed 13 May 2014).

Jonah

Introduction

Jonah is both a familiar and a very unfamiliar story. It's one of the most common Bible stories to be retold in children's books, and yet we very rarely find the whole thing: writers tend to enjoy the fun part with the whale, but they leave the part with the plant and worm off the end. This means that the final moral of the story is changed: children who know the story will often think that Jonah was scared to go to Nineveh (or just disobedient) but found out that if he didn't do what God said, he'd be forced to do it in the end. This is not actually the case. Jonah's reason for not going to Nineveh is more complicated and involves a lesson about accepting God's grace and forgiveness for other people as well as for himself; and God doesn't just force him to get the job done, but gently guides him towards understanding the reasons for his task.

Story

God said to Jonah,
'Got to go to Nineveh,
got to tell the people there
I've got something to say.'
But Jonah didn't want to,
Jonah was a scaredy-pants,
Jonah didn't fancy it,
so Jonah ran away!

Shhhh, shhhh! Jonah ran away!

Jonah did a runner,
sailed into the sunset,
thought he'd have some fun
somewhere nice and warm.
God saw him scram,
had another plan,
God stretched out his hand
and sent along a storm!

Crash, flash! God sent along a storm.
Shhh, shhh! Jonah ran away!

Sailors saw the sky,
thought they were going to die,
Jonah had a lie-down
feeling rather pale.
Then he told them all:
'Throw me overboard,
I've sinned against the Lord',
so God sent along a whale!

Glop, glop! God sent along a whale.
Crash, flash! God sent along a storm.
Shhh, shhh! Jonah ran away!

Jonah's rather smelly
sitting in the belly
of a giant whale, he
couldn't take it any more,
so he started prayin',
turned to God again;
the whale got a pain
and it sicked him onto shore.

Bleaurgh! The whale sicked him onto shore!

Glop, glop! God sent along a whale.
Crash, flash! God sent along a storm.
Shhh, shhh! Jonah ran away!

Jonah's quickly learning
he'd better try returning,
to Nineveh he journeyed
and he began to shout:
'You're not being good,
not doing what you should
and you're offending God,
so you'd better sort it out!'

Tut tut tut, you'd better sort it out.
Bleaurgh! The whale sicked him onto shore!
Glop, glop! God sent along a whale.
Crash, flash! God sent along a storm.
Shhh, shhh! Jonah ran away!

Everyone was sorry,
they were really worried,
so the people hurried
to do as Jonah said.
God was understanding
but Jonah started ranting,
had a proper tantrum
and wished that he was dead.

Moan, groan! He wished that he was dead.
Tut tut tut, you'd better sort it out.
Bleaurgh! The whale sicked him onto shore!
Glop, glop! God sent along a whale.
Crash, flash! God sent along a storm.
Shhh, shhh! Jonah ran away!

Jonah started yelling:
'What's the point of telling
people they're rebelling
then forgiving everyone?!'
God saw he'd need a lesson
to get the right impression,
took him to the desert
and sat him in the sun.

Shine, shine, God sat him in the sun.
Moan, groan! He wished that he was dead.
Tut tut tut, you'd better sort it out.
Bleaurgh! The whale sicked him onto shore!
Glop, glop! God sent along a whale.
Crash, flash! God sent along a storm.
Shhh, shhh! Jonah ran away!

The heat made Jonah pant
until he was too hot to rant;
God sent along a plant
to grow above his head.
Once Jonah's head was chillier,
God sent along a killer,
a little caterpillar
which chewed the plant to shreds.

Munch, munch, the plant was chewed to shreds.
Shine, shine, God sat him in the sun.
Moan, groan! He wished that he was dead.
Tut tut tut, you'd better sort it out.
Bleaurgh! The whale sicked him onto shore!
Glop, glop! God sent along a whale.
Crash, flash! God sent along a storm.
Shhh, shhh! Jonah ran away!

Jonah started crying
because his plant was dying;
when God heard him sighing
he said: 'Jonah, now you see
if you're feeling sour
about a little flower,
how much more did Nineveh
mean a lot to me?'

'Everyone in Nineveh means a lot to me!'

And now we're going to see if we can do all the noises in the right order to tell the story.

Shhh, shhh! Jonah ran away!
Crash, flash! God sent along a storm.
Glop, glop! God sent along a whale.
Bleaurgh! The whale sicked him onto shore!
Tut tut tut, you'd better sort it out.
Moan, groan! He wished that he was dead.
Shine, shine, God sat him in the sun.
Munch, munch, the plant was chewed to shreds.
Everyone in Nineveh means a lot to me!

Notes for storytellers

This can be used as either a song or a performance poem. The idea is that the children join in with the noises, adding one to the refrain after every verse. You can either teach them each noise as you go along or teach them all together at the beginning. At the end of the story, the challenge is to go through all the noises and actions again but backwards, which puts them in the right order to retell the story. As in the video, you could try gradually adding to a picture board to help the children out with this visually, and then you only have to point to the pictures in the opposite order at the end.

The backing track for this song is available at www.kevinmayhew.com/jesse-videos.

From screen to stage

This song is even more fun when everybody joins in. Make sure you invite your audience to take part in the refrain, and encourage them along the first few times to ensure maximum participation by the time it gets really silly! The more children there are in your audience, the less persuasion they will need. They tend to make the vomit noise, in particular, with great enthusiasm.

It may help everyone's memories to add an action to each noise, and to introduce and rehearse each new noise and action briefly before launching into the new verse.

Bible references

Jonah has a book of the Bible all to himself.

Decoration

A whale; a plant and a worm; a boat.

What next?

Jonah explores themes of journey, calling, obedience, faith and forgiveness. The story is also about tolerance: God's message to Jonah is that the people of Nineveh are worth loving and saving, even though they are 'different' and seem to be 'bad'. It's a great story to introduce any discussion along the lines of difference and acceptance.

One of the text types that children study in Key Stage 2 literacy is that of persuasive texts, and this story is full of persuasion! Jonah is called to persuade the Ninevites to repent, while God persuades Jonah to his point of view using images, almost like little parables, found in nature: the storm, the whale, the hot sun, the plant and the worm. Children could choose a subject for their own persuasive text – perhaps an environmental issue such as littering – and think of a story that would make their point.

Isaiah

Introduction

It would be strange to have a Jesse Tree without introducing the very passage from which the tree takes its name. However, if you have time to dwell on Isaiah for a little longer, do have a look at a few more of his messianic prophecies, especially those that we are used to hearing at Christmas and Easter. There are some suggestions in the Bible references section.

Story

Isaiah was a prophet. We've met prophets before in some of the other tales from the Jesse Tree: Samuel, Elijah and Jonah. They are people who hear from God and have to pass the message on. They are people with a very hard job to do.

Isaiah has a whole book to himself in the Bible. He lived during a time when God's people barely remembered that they were God's people any more. There were wars and defeats and breaking of God's commandments. God told Isaiah to give a lot of bad news to his people: things would get a lot worse before they would get better. But in between all the bad news, God gave Isaiah some beautiful, peaceful words about what the world was really supposed to be like, and how it would be like that again one day. And it all seemed to have something to do with a person, somebody who would somehow be related to — guess who? Jesse. The one our tree is named after. In fact, Isaiah was the first person to talk about a Jesse Tree! He said:

The people of Israel are like a tree that has been cut down, but its roots remain in the earth.

A new leaf shall come out of the tree of Jesse;

a new branch shall grow out of his roots.

The spirit of God will be with him,

he will be wise and understanding,

he will be wise and mighty,

he will be wise and he will delight in God.

His kingdom will be so peaceful that the wolf shall live with the lamb,

the cow and the bear shall eat grass together,

children shall play with snakes and not be hurt.

No one will ever be hurt or destroyed on my holy mountain,

says God.

Notes for storytellers

Passages of the Bible which are not stories can be very difficult to put across effectively to a young audience. There are several solutions, which include constructing a story around the passage (see how the psalm was presented in Story 18), exploring the passage in a more fluid way (for example, through use of a story bag as in Story 2) or simplifying the passage and putting it in context, as above. It's important for children to see somebody actually open a Bible at some point, both to begin to understand where these stories come from, and to become familiar with the way the Bible is read in a church. This is a great opportunity to do that. It is also important for children to be introduced to the concept of the Bible as a library of books containing many different kinds of writing, hence this short explanation of Isaiah's prophecies.

From screen to stage

A simple way of making a Bible reading more interactive is to ask the congregation to listen out for certain words – preferably repeated words – and to demonstrate when they hear them by performing an action. In this case, for example, you could ask your listeners to make a sign for the word 'wise' and another for the word 'God'. In a livelier reading or with younger children, you could also ask for a corresponding animal noise every time you say the name of an animal, perhaps holding up a soft toy or a picture of the animal when it appears in the passage.

Bible references

The reading was paraphrased from Isaiah 11:1-9. Other readings from Isaiah which are particularly relevant to Christmas are 7:13-15, in which Isaiah foretells that a virgin will give birth to Immanuel; 9:1-7, in which the people who walked in darkness have seen a great light and Isaiah lists some of the names for Jesus; and 40:3-5, in which Isaiah foretells the voice of John the Baptist in the wilderness.

Decoration

A leaf; a tree; a tree stump; a new plant growing.

What next?

An important part of teaching the Bible in the RE curriculum is to explore how, rather than being a single religious book, the Bible is a library of texts which have different genres, audiences and purposes.

One way to start this discussion could be to ask the children to sort a collection of texts including letters and postcards, story and poetry books, encyclopedias, recipes, shopping lists, instructions from games and from flat packs, advice slips from boxes of painkillers, advertisements, newspapers, magazines and warning posters. Do any of them go together? Which genres are similar? Which audiences are they intended for, and for what purposes? Which ones are trustworthy? Are any of them more relevant to life, or more important than others?

How many different kinds of writing do the children already know about from the Bible? There are stories and poetry, instructions and lists, eyewitness accounts and prophecies, and some parts which are a mixture of several of these!

Ask the children to compile their own collections of texts: if they could choose a selection to put into one folder to take to a desert island, what would they include? Some things might be useful, others entertaining, others chosen for sentimental value or linked to memories such as a letter from a parent. All these reasons are valid for texts in the Bible as well.

Jeremiah

Introduction

Jeremiah is another prophet, and these verses are linked in the Jesse Tree to the stories about God's covenant with his people (see Noah, and later Moses, and Joshua and the Ark of the Covenant). Here, Jeremiah writes about a new covenant promised by God to replace and renew the old one which has been broken by Israel. Christians believe that this refers to a time that begins with the death and resurrection of Jesus.

Story

I will write my law on your hearts,
I will write my law on your hearts,
I will write my law on your hearts,
you will be my people and I will be your God.

And I will forgive your sins
and not remember them any more;
yes, I will forgive your sins:
Jeremiah thirty-one, thirty-three to thirty-four!

Actions (to be taught first):

For the first three lines, pretend to write on your hand and then cross your hands over your heart.

In the fourth line, point forwards for 'you', to yourself for 'my and 'I', and upwards for 'God'.

The second part uses an approximation of British Sign Language for 'forgive' (rubbing a fist over a palm as if cleaning it) and 'forget' (a closed fist held next to the temple, then moved away and opened).

In the final line, one hand holds up three fingers while the other hand holds up one, then three, then four fingers. Getting into a tangle at this point is all part of the fun.

Notes for storytellers

In Story 21, we saw a few ways of presenting a Bible passage that is not a story, and this is another one: a simple action song which serves as a memory aid for a verse that comes directly from the Bible.

From screen to stage

The song is short enough to take time teaching both the actions and the tune, and then to sing it through a few times – enough times for a congregation to stop learning it and start enjoying it. It is also short enough not to need accompaniment, although the backing track is available at www.kevinmayhew.com/jesse-videos if you wish to use it.

Bible references

As the song says, the words are taken from Jeremiah 31:33-34. It is quoted again, and explained a little, in the New Testament in Hebrews 10:16, 17, in which the writer implies that Jeremiah was foretelling the work of the Holy Spirit when he talked about the law being written on our hearts. Paul might also be recalling the same verse in chapter 2 of Romans, when he explains that even people who don't live under the law have a conscience, which is the law written on their hearts.

Decoration

A heart, perhaps with a scroll, book or writing on it.

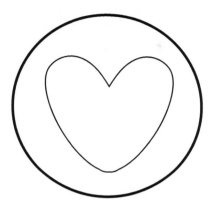

What next?

Story 11 has already led into a discussion about rules, but these verses refer more to conscience and the knowledge of right and wrong: what is it, apart from written rules, that teaches us how to treat other people? Older children might like to look at the rules, cultures and traditions of other countries and faiths, noticing similarities and differences and discovering which morals unite the whole human race.

Children could make and decorate origami or cardboard hearts before writing on them: they could choose to write something that they feel is especially important, such as a rule that they would like to remember or Jesus' summary of the commandments: 'Love the Lord your God with all your heart, soul and mind, and love your neighbour as yourself' (Matthew 22:37-39). Two rules for the heart.

John the Baptist

Introduction

The third week of Advent traditionally remembers John the Baptist, the cousin of Jesus who was born to announce the coming of the Christ, and who eventually baptised Jesus. Mary's visit to the pregnant Elizabeth, when John recognises Jesus although they are both still inside their mothers' wombs, is a part of the Christmas story. Although the traditional Advent reading about John is his calling in the wilderness, for the Jesse Tree I have chosen his special birth, announced by an angel only a few months before Gabriel's more famous announcement to Mary.

Story

Zachariah was in the temple one day,
when an angel said, 'Zach, don't be **glum**.
You know your wife Elizabeth?
She's going to be a **mum**!'
'I'm not so sure,' said Zachariah,
'She's not as young as **some**.'
'Don't question God!' the angel said,
and he struck Zachariah **dumb**.
When people asked him what he'd seen,
poor Zach could just say, '**Um . . .**'
But still he managed to tell his tale
making gestures with his **thumb**.

Until the baby, John, was born,
Zach's jaws were stuck like **gum**,
but when at last he spoke again,
he proclaimed, 'The Lord will **come**!'

Actions (to be taught first):

glum: fold arms, stick out bottom lip
mum: mime holding a baby, or make a round pregnant belly shape with hands
some: count on fingers
dumb: zip mouth shut
Um: hand under chin as if thinking, or scratch head
thumb: hold up thumb
gum: mime pulling bubble gum out of mouth
come: beckon from above

Notes for storytellers

There has already been an example of this special form of performance poetry, in Story 10. Each line of the poem is repeated three times, allowing for changes in emphasis and giving plenty of opportunity for the children to join in with the actions.

From screen to stage

As in Story 10, this form of poetry requires audience participation, especially when it comes to remembering and joining in with the rhyming words and actions. Teaching the words and actions beforehand may mean that a congregation can guess them even before you've said them the first time, and the way they have been fitted in to the story sometimes raises a laugh. Make the actions very big and goofy for added effect.

Bible references

The story of the angel visiting Zachariah can be found in Luke 1:5-24, and the birth of John the Baptist in Luke 1:57-80, which includes Zachariah's prophetic hymn of praise after his voice has been returned to him. John reappears as a grown man in Luke 3, and baptises his cousin Jesus.

Decoration

A dove over water; a lamb and tall cross, the symbol for John the Baptist; a scallop shell; a mouth zipped up or a face with a hand over the mouth.

What next?

Can the children communicate without using their voices? Ask them to pretend that they are Zachariah and have to give Elizabeth the message that he has seen an angel and that she is going to have a baby. Depending on their age and the part of the curriculum you would like to explore, they could mime, write a letter, draw some pictures or make a model.

Mary

Introduction

The traditional beginning of the Christmas story is the appearance of the angel Gabriel to Mary. This moment beloved of Nativity plays has found a fresh perspective in Chip Colquhoun's hilarious puppet sketch.

Story

Four Told
by Chip Colquhoun

GRACE (a female puppet) should be dressed up as Mary. GABRIEL (a real person) should ideally be wearing something recognisable from school Nativities as a generic angel costume.

GABRIEL: Right, Grace, are you ready?

GRACE: I'm not Grace; I'm Mary!

GABRIEL: Great, you're already getting into character! Now –

GRACE: Character? What does 'character' mean? We haven't invented drama yet. Or at least I don't think we have . . . Have we?

GABRIEL: Well –

GRACE: Actually, have we invented English yet? Shouldn't we be talking in Israelese or something?

GABRIEL: Grace, we're acting. That means we're trying to tell the story of what happened so that people can understand it. We're not trying to make it exactly the same.

GRACE: Oh . . . We're not?

GABRIEL: No. We couldn't even if we wanted to, 'cause we weren't there, were we? Even the gospel writer Luke wasn't there, and he had to hear the story from someone else after he'd met Jesus. So we have to imagine what the real Mary would have felt like, and show those feelings in a way that all the children here can understand.

GRACE: Ah, I see. OK.

GABRIEL: Right. So, are you ready?

GRACE: Yes. I'm ready.

GABRIEL: OK . . . Greetings, most highly favoured lady! I am the angel Gabriel, and I bring you good news!

Throughout GRACE's next line, GABRIEL should be attempting to interrupt her with gradually increasing urgency – until his scripted exclamation.

GRACE: *(With excessive joy)* Oh, brilliant! Oh thank you! Oh, this is the bestest day of my life so far ever! I can't wait to tell everyone! I feel so honoured! So overwhelmed! So on top of the world with a triple chocolate fudge brownie ice-cream so high it's gonna touch the moon and make it explode into a shower of cute little fluffy bunnies that smile and sing 'You Don't Know You're Beautiful' as they gently float to the –

GABRIEL: Graaace!

GRACE: What?

GABRIEL: That's not quite how it went.

GRACE: Well, I know that! You told me to act the way Mary would have felt.

GABRIEL: That's right, but Mary didn't feel quite so . . . happy as that.

GRACE: She didn't? But it was really good news!

GABRIEL: Well, yes, we know that *now*, but back then the sight of an angel was pretty scary. The Bible says that when Mary saw Gabriel, she was 'greatly troubled'. So try being a little more worried.

GRACE: Oh . . . OK! Can we go from the beginning again then?

GABRIEL: OK. Are you ready?

GRACE: OK.

GABRIEL: OK. Greetings, most high —

Throughout GRACE's next line, GABRIEL should be attempting to calm her – without success.

GRACE: AAAAAAAAAAAHH!!! Oh my word, what is it?! Is it a ghost?! Is it an alien?! It just appeared! It's got wings! It can fly! It can speak! It can fly and speak at the same time! It's a multitasking alien ghost thing with wings! What do I do?!

GABRIEL: *(Beat)* Um . . . Do not be afraid.

GRACE: *(Breaking out of character)* What? But you told me Mary was supposed to be afraid!

GABRIEL: No no no, that's what Gabriel said to her: 'Do not be afraid.'

GRACE: Oh, OK. Um . . . *(Becoming Mary again)* What?! What do you want?!

GABRIEL: Mary, you have found favour with God. He is going to let you be the mother of his son, and you shall call him Jesus —

Again throughout GRACE's next line, GABRIEL should be attempting to interrupt her with gradually increasing urgency – until his scripted exclamation.

GRACE: What?! Oh my life, I'm gonna have a baby! But I'm not even married! We don't have the money! What's Joseph gonna say?! What's my mum gonna say?! Will she like the name Jesus?! Where will we go?! The hospitals don't even have ultrasound yet! I'm too young! I won't be able to go to university! I won't be able to get a job! I don't even know the right temperature for a milk bottle! I don't even know if we've invented milk bottles yet!

GABRIEL: Graaaaaace!

GRACE: What? What now?

GABRIEL: I don't think Mary was that scared.

GRACE: Are you sure? I think I'd be that scared if it was me!

GABRIEL: Well, maybe. But the Bible doesn't say that Mary heard the news and went off her trolley.

GRACE: Well, of course not. They hadn't invented trolleys yet.

GABRIEL: No. Y – No! Look, Mary was troubled, but she was also patient enough to listen to what Gabriel had to say. She couldn't really believe her eyes, or her ears. I expect it was just . . . really very confusing!

GRACE: Oh . . . So you want me to be confused?

GABRIEL: That might work a bit better, yeah. Shall we try it?

GRACE: OK. I'm ready.

GABRIEL: Good. Right then . . . Greetings, most highly favoured lady! I am the angel Gabriel, and I bring you good news! Do not be afraid, for you have found favour with God. He is going to let you be the mother of his son, and you shall call him Jesus.

GRACE is staring at GABRIEL with her jaw hanging open.

GABRIEL: Uh . . . Mary?

GRACE: *(Beat)* Huh?

GABRIEL: No no no . . . Grace, Mary wasn't that confused!

GRACE: She wasn't?! Oh, I don't know what to do! She's getting exciting news, but I can't be too excited! The news was terrifying, but I can't be too terrified! The news was confusing, but I can't be too confused! It's like . . . It's like when I had to move school!

GABRIEL: What do you mean?

GRACE: Well, you remember when I had to move school? I was really excited, 'cause I was going to be making new friends. But I was also really upset, because I had to say goodbye to my old friends. And I was really nervous because I didn't know what to expect! I had all those feelings, good and bad . . . all at the same time! What do you do when that happens?

GABRIEL: Well, why don't you do what Mary did?

GRACE: Huh? What was that?

GABRIEL: Well, Mary decided to trust in God. She was excited, and she was also scared, but she knew that – if it was all God's plan – she could trust that it would all be OK in the end.

GRACE: So . . . I should just trust in God?

GABRIEL: Exactly.

GRACE: OK then. I'll give that a try!

GABRIEL: Good! Let's give it a go, then . . . Greetings, most highly favoured lady! I am the angel Gabriel, and I bring you good news! Do not be afraid, for you have found favour with God. He is going to let you be the mother of his son, and you shall call him Jesus.

GRACE: I am God's servant. May everything you say come true.

GABRIEL: And that, Grace, was your bestest acting ever. Well done.

Notes for storytellers

A sketch is always a good way to put a story across. A puppet sketch is sometimes even better, because a puppet is larger than life: it can be sillier, funnier and much more wrong than a real person without causing offence, and so a message can be presented even more clearly. Here, Grace needs a lot of correction of her assumptions about Mary, but she eventually finds a way to explain all her emotions in a way that children can easily understand.

From screen to stage

This sketch could be performed by a person and a puppet, two puppets, or two people. Make sure that Grace's overacting shows a very different emotion each time, and expect lots of laughs – but take your time over the more serious discussion at the end.

Bible references

The Annunciation takes place in Luke 1:26-39.

Decoration

An angel; Mary; the word 'Yes'.

What next?

Can the children think of a time when, like Grace, they had lots of different feelings all at once? How did it all work out? How difficult would it have been to trust in God?

Christmas Day

Introduction

This fun puppet song brings together some of the characters from the Jesse Tree. In the stories, we have seen God's relationship with lots of different people through the history of the Bible. This song finishes that journey by celebrating the event which was God's call to everyone in every time and place.

Story

Christmas Called the World
by Chip Colquhoun

If you wanna make a donkey move, put a carrot on a stick.
If you wanna get a dog to sit, you just say 'Sit!'
But say, 'Sit,' to a donkey and he'll just stand there.
Give a dog a carrot and he'll just stare . . .

Some people are like Abraham.
God made him a promise; he said 'Here I am!'
But Moses needed a bigger push,
so God had to shout from a burning bush.
Everybody's different, so how do you call them all?
(Gotta call them all, gotta call them all.)

But everybody listens to a baby's cry.
You know what a baby needs and so do I.
When God held out a human hand and asked us all to love,
everyone could understand and offer up our hearts.

With a baby's cry
Christmas called the world.

If you wanna keep some chickens safe, keep them in a little hut.
If you wanna tell a camel where to go, give the reins a little tug.
But a hut holding a camel will just get wrecked.
And try to tug a chick and you'll just get pecked . . .

Some people are like Zachariah –
speechless till he stopped callin' God a liar.
But Jonah chose to keep resistin',
so God had to stick him in a whale's intestine.
Everybody's different, so how do you call them all?
(Gotta call them all, gotta call them all.)

But everybody listens to a baby's cry.
You know what a baby needs and so do I.
When God held out a human hand and asked us all to love,
everyone could understand and offer up our hearts.
With a baby's cry
Christmas called the world.

Notes for storytellers

This puppet song was choreographed and performed with home-made signs and props in order to be within the scope of most church puppet teams. If you are interested in learning more about puppetry, have a look at *Performing with Puppets: A Puppeteer's Guide.*[7]

From screen to stage

The backing track for this song is available at www.kevinmayhew.com/jesse-videos.

---

7. Amy Robinson, *Performing with Puppets: A Puppeteer's Guide* (Kevin Mayhew, 2013).

Bible references

The Nativity story can be found in Matthew 1:18–2:12 and Luke 2:1-20. Matthew and Luke each describe different events: Luke has the angels and shepherds, and Matthew the wise men.

Decoration

A baby; a Nativity scene

What next?

Have fun celebrating Christmas Day – Happy Christmas!

Acknowledgements

It's in the nature of storytelling to hear and watch other people telling stories and to tuck away their ideas and techniques in a back pocket to be brought out and reused later. Undoubtedly there are many storytellers who have unwittingly contributed to the tales in this book, but particular thanks must go to Bob Hartman for his inspiring performances and friendly encouragement – not to mention his generous contribution of an entire new form of narrative poetry, and a kind foreword.

Thanks, too, to my friend and colleague Chip Colquhoun, not only for his puppet sketch, musical contributions and video performances but for being such a tinder box of ideas and new approaches over the years. All kinds of concepts found in these retellings were originally invented or refined with or by Chip. The idea of using a balloon as Goliath's head was one of his.

Thanks to Anna Harwich for singing and for being willing to undergo a crash course in puppetry at short notice, to Hari Sharma for being such a competent young puppeteer and to Rochelle King for cameo appearances as well as skilful editing. Thanks to Ed Heathcote for having the patience of Job through many, many takes.

All stories need a testing ground. Thanks to the staff and children at Rattlesden Primary School, Centre Academy and Old Buckenham Hall for test running final versions and allowing the cameras in to record live performances. Finally, thanks to GenR8, XcelR8 and the Mothers' Union, in whose publications several of these ideas appeared first in some form.

Tales
from the
Jesse
Tree